BLUEPRINT

Design & Technology
Teacher's Resource
Book
Key Stage 2

Kate Bennington

Stanley Thornes (Publishers) Ltd

Do you receive *BLUEPRINTS NEWS*?

Blueprints is an expanding series of practical teacher's ideas books and photocopiable resources for use in primary schools. Books are available for separate infant and junior age ranges for every core and foundation subject, as well as for an ever widening range of other primary teaching needs. These include **Blueprints Primary English** books and **Blueprints Resource Banks**. **Blueprints** are carefully structured around the demands of National Curriculum in England and Wales, but are used successfully by schools and teachers in Scotland, Northern Ireland and elsewhere.

Blueprints provide:
- *Total curriculum coverage*
- *Hundreds of practical ideas*
- *Books specifically for the age range you teach*
- *Flexible resources for the whole school or for individual teachers*
- *Excellent photocopiable sheets – ideal for assessment and children's work profiles*
- *Supreme value.*

Books may be bought by credit card over the telephone and information obtained on **(01242) 577944**. Alternatively, photocopy and return this **FREEPOST** form to receive **Blueprints News**, our regular update on all new and existing titles. You may also like to add the name of a friend who would be interested in being on the mailing list.

Please add my name to the **BLUEPRINTS NEWS** mailing list.

Mr/Mrs/Miss/Ms _____

Home address _____

_____ Postcode _____

School address _____

_____ Postcode _____

Please also send **BLUEPRINTS NEWS** to:

Mr/Mrs/Miss/Ms _____

Address _____

_____ Postcode _____

To: Marketing Services Dept., Stanley Thornes Ltd, FREEPOST (GR 782), Cheltenham, GL50 1BR

Text © Kate Bennington 1996
Original line illustrations by Mark Dunn, © ST(P) Ltd 1996

The author would like to acknowledge the help and support of the Rutherford Appleton Laboratories, Parsons Down Junior School, the Berkshire Design Technology team, her family and friends, and above all, her husband, Steve.

Material from the National Curriculum is Crown copyright and is reproduced with the permission of the Controller of Her Majesty's Stationery Office.

First published in 1996 by:
Stanley Thornes (Publishers) Ltd
Ellenborough House
Wellington Street
CHELTENHAM GL50 1YW
England

A catalogue record for this book is available from the British Library.
ISBN 0-7487-2884-8

Typeset by Tech Set Limited, Gateshead, Tyne & Wear
Printed and bound in Great Britain by
Redwood Books, Trowbridge, Wiltshire

98 99 00 / 10 9 8 7 6 5 4 3 2

CONTENTS

* suitable for lower KS2
▼ suitable for upper KS2

INTRODUCTION

My aim in writing these books is to provide teachers of Key Stage 2 Design & Technology (both specialist and non-specialist) with a wide range of activities and techniques that fulfill the requirements of the National Curriculum Guidelines for this subject area.

Blueprints: Design & Technology Teacher's Resource Book Key Stage 2

This book adopts a skills-based approach to the teaching of Design & Technology in order to provide the children with opportunities to develop the skills required to use the range of materials and components outlined in the National Curriculum Guidelines. The main section of the book is divided into Units of work, each providing ideas for project work that relate to a distinct area of study, e.g. Unit 8: Wheels/axles. The project work has been carefully designed to cover a range of skills, and the children are required to research, investigate, experiment, design, make and evaluate. For each project within a Unit of work there is a more detailed list of the skills that are to be covered — the learning objectives. This is followed by a list of key vocabulary. There is then a logical sequence of tasks – Investigating tasks and Focused practical tasks — that are intended to provide the children with the necessary skills and information to complete the Design and make assignment that concludes each section of work. Each of these assignments requires that the children design and make a product to a specific brief. They are then given opportunities to evaluate their work. According to the resources available, the children could work through each project as a whole class or in smaller groups. It is intended that each project should provide a whole term's work. However, ideas can be taken out of the termly units and adapted to suit other DT topics and/or other subject areas.

To attempt the project work suggested in this book, the children will need to have had some previous experience of technology. To enable the teacher to select work suitable for the ability of their group, I have indicated those Units of work that are more suitable for lower Key Stage 2 and those more suitable for upper Key Stage 2. The Units of work designed for lower Key Stage 2 are more teacher-directed, progressing to activities requiring less guidance for upper Key Stage 2. (The Units of work are appropriately coded on the Contents page of the Teacher's Resource Book.)

Techniques, tools and storage

This section outlines basic designing and making techniques covered in the project work. (These should prove particularly useful to the non-specialist teacher.) Also, advice is offered on the safe use of tools in the classroom, as well as storage ideas for resources.

Resources checklist

This section provides a checklist of useful classroom resources including consumable materials — that will support Key Stage 2 Design & Technology.

Blueprints: Design & Technology Copymasters Key Stage 2

This book provides a wide range of photocopiable sheets to support the activities in the Teacher's Resource Book. Many of the sheets are examples of the sort of work which can be done, and they can be adapted or new ideas added to suit your particular needs.

ENGLAND, WALES AND SCOTLAND: DESIGN & TECHNOLOGY CURRICULUM GUIDELINES

National Curriculum for England and Wales Key Stage 2 Programme of Study	National Guidelines for Scotland	Units of work in which skills are used
1. Pupils should be given opportunities to develop their design and technology capability through:		
assignments in which they design and make products		
focused practical tasks		
activities in which they investigate, disassemble and evaluate simple products.		
2. Pupils should be given opportunities to: work with a range of materials and components	Encourage pupils to explore and subsequently identify the varying characteristics of a given range of materials.	
work independently and in teams	Some modelling and constructing activities should be undertaken as group enterprises.	
apply skills, knowledge and understanding from the Programmes of Study of other subjects.	Links with activities in other curricular areas should be maintained and developed.	
3. Designing skills Pupils should be taught to:		
use information sources to help their designing	observe and record from given sources model and construct from observed objects, produce work from previously observed, recorded and collected information	Pop-up cards, A shelter for a castaway, Bridges/playground equipment, Chunky fruit fool, Lollipop-stick puppets, A 2D chassis
generate ideas – considering users and purposes for which they are designing	Their studies should include some consideration of social, environmental and economic factors.	All units
clarify ideas, develop criteria for their designs and suggest ways forward	The pupils should be led to understand how to tackle a design task, and how to collaborate in planning an outcome to a specified remit. The teacher should provide tasks specified in the form of a brief.	A shelter for a castaway, Wall-hangings, Fabric-covered boxes, Picnic lunch, 'Tap turners'
consider appearance, function, safety and reliability when developing proposals	select the most suitable idea and produce a prototype	Forex clocks, A shelter for a castaway, Christmas decorations, Wall-hangings, Fabric-covered boxes, A light for a teenage doll, 'Tap turners', A 2D chassis, Advertising signs
explore, develop and communicate aspects of their design by modelling their ideas in a variety of ways	suggest by drawing, visual presentation and simple models at least one possible solution to a design problem Objects should be observed, drawn, sketched and modelled in a variety of media	Modelling in paper/card — Pop-up cards, Wall-hangings Modelling in clay — Christmas decorations Construction kit modelling — A shelter for a castaway, Bridges/playground equipment
develop a clear idea of what has to be done, proposing a sequence of actions, and suggesting alternative ways of proceeding if things go wrong	show an ability to plan ahead — selecting, organising and controlling materials in order to solve a specified problem or task	Forex Clocks, Fabric-covered boxes, Picnic lunch, Chunky fruit fool, Traffic lights, A 2D chassis, Correx toys, Roundabouts
evaluate their design ideas as these develop, bearing in mind the users and purposes for which the product is intended, and indicate ways of improving their ideas.	Pupils should be invited to evaluate: how they have responded to a design brief, indicating difficulties in the design process, evaluating their own design work, showing an understanding of a design process, and indicating modifications where appropriate	Fabric-covered boxes, Chunky fruit fool, Picnic lunch, Traffic lights, A 2D chassis, Advertising signs
4. Making skills Pupils should be taught to:		
select appropriate materials, tools and techniques	Activities will lead to consideration of suitability of materials, scale and function. Show an ability to plan ahead — selecting, organising and controlling materials in order to solve a specified problem or task.	All units

National Curriculum for England and Wales Key Stage 2 Programme of Study	National Guidelines for Scotland	Units of work in which skills are used
measure, mark out, cut and shape a range of materials using additional tools, equipment and techniques		Pop-up cards, Christmas decorations, Wall-hangings, Fabric-covered boxes, Chunky fruit fool, Picnic lunch, Lollipop-stick puppets, A 2D chassis, Correx toys, Roundabouts
join and combine materials and components accurately in temporary and permanent ways		All units
apply additional finishing techniques appropriate to the materials being used and the purpose of the product		Forex clocks, A shelter for a castaway, Bridges/playground equipment, Fabric-covered boxes, Chunky fruit fool, Minibeasts
develop a clear idea of what has to be done, planning how to use materials, equipment and processes, and suggesting alternative methods of making if first attempts fail	Pupils should become familiar with the process of working from ideas through to solutions. Pupils should be led to understand a process-based approach to solving problems or design tasks.	Forex clocks, Bridges/playground equipment, Wall-hangings, Chunky fruit fool, Picnic lunch, A 2D chassis, Correx toys, Roundabouts
evaluate their products, identifying strengths and weaknesses, and carrying out appropriate tests	Pupils should be invited to evaluate how they have responded to a design brief, indicating difficulties in the design process and the success or otherwise of the task.	Pop-up cards, Forex clocks, A shelter for a castaway, Bridges, Chunky fruit fool, Picnic lunch, A light for a teenage doll, Traffic lights, Correx toys
implement improvements they have identified.		All units
5. Knowledge and understanding Pupils should be taught:		
how the working characteristics of materials relate to the ways materials are used	solve problems by selecting and organising two- and three-dimensional materials from a given range identify the varying characteristics of a range of materials	Christmas decorations, Wall-hangings, Fabric-covered boxes, Chunky fruit fool, Picnic lunch, Correx toys
how materials can be combined and mixed in order to create more useful properties	consider, select and use a range of media, occasionally combining some of these; exploring these materials and how they are cut, shaped, joined and decorated	A shelter for castaway, Bridges/playground equipment, Fabric-covered boxes, Chunky fruit fool, Picnic lunch
how simple mechanisms can be used to produce different types of movement	In investigating and recording, pupils should be encouraged to explore the structure of natural and manufactured objects.	Pop-up cards, Lollipop-stick puppets, 'Tap turners', A 2D chassis, Correx toys, Roundabouts, Advertising signs, Minibeasts
how electrical circuits, including those with simple switches, can be used to achieve functional results		A light for a teenage doll, Traffic lights, Advertising signs
how structures can fail when loaded, and techniques for reinforcing and strengthening them	Three-dimensional work involving construction techniques should be explored.	A shelter for a castaway, Bridges/playground equipment
to investigate, disassemble and evaluate simple products and appliances, including those with mechanical and electrical components, in order to learn how they function		All units
to relate the way things work to their intended purpose — how materials and components have been used, people's needs, and what users say about them	opportunities for pupils to extend their insight into techniques	A light for a teenage doll, 'Tap turners', A 2D chassis, Correx toys, Roundabouts
to distinguish between how well a product has been made and how well it has been designed		Wall-hangings, Fabric-covered boxes, Chunky fruit fool, Picnic lunch, Lollipop-stick puppets, 'Tap turners'
to consider the effectiveness of a product, including the extent to which it meets a clear need (is fit for a purpose), and uses resources appropriately	Examples of 'models' from the world of professional design may be used as stimulating resources.	Pop-up cards, Christmas decorations, Fabric-covered boxes, Correx toys, Advertising signs
further knowledge and understanding of health and safety as designers, makers and consumers		All units
to use the appropriate vocabulary for naming and describing the equipment, materials and components, and the processes they use.	opportunities for the pupils to extend their understanding and use of appropriate vocabulary	All units

UNIT 1: USING SHEET MATERIALS

POP-UP CARDS

Learning objectives

Designing skills
The children should be given the opportunity to:

● research pop-up cards and books, in order to gather information about their mechanisms and design
● draw an exploded diagram
● model design ideas using paper
● design a card and envelope for a specific occasion and recipient.

Making skills
The children should be encouraged to:

● practise marking out and cutting paper and card
● demonstrate their ability to fold accurately and score paper and card
● create a simple folded-hinge mechanism
● achieve a good quality finish.

Knowledge and understanding
The children should be given the opportunity to:

● examine a range of cards and register their likes and dislikes
● investigate a number of similar pop-up mechanisms
● consider whether cards are suitable for their intended recipient and occasion.

Vocabulary: fold, score, cut, measure, mechanism, tabs.

INVESTIGATING TASKS

Materials/equipment needed: a selection of greetings cards (without pop-up mechanisms); pop-up cards and books; drawing equipment; envelopes.

Task 1

Introduce the project by discussing the different occasions on which a card might be sent. Initially, talk about common celebrations, e.g. birthdays, and general occasions, e.g. passing exams or a driving test. Then explain that many religious festivals are marked by sending cards, e.g. Diwali and Passover.

Task 2

Divide the class into groups, and give each group a set of at least four different greetings cards. Each set should include a variety of cards designed for specific occasions. (They do not need to be pop-up cards.) Ask each group to decide who their cards have been designed for and on which occasions they would be sent. They will probably have little difficulty deciding the purpose of those cards that have writing inside or on the front of them. However, more general cards — e.g. those with a picture and no words — should prove to be more of a challenge for them.

When all the groups have finished this task, ask for a volunteer from each group. S/he should choose two of the group's cards and say why and to whom the group thought each would be sent. The volunteer should then try to explain how they reached these conclusions. Try to focus the discussion on the characteristics of the recipient, in preparation for later work.

Task 3

The children should remain in groups for this task. Provide each group with a pop-up book to examine, and ask them to decide who their book has been designed for. (Most books of this type are intended for very young children.) Then encourage them to look carefully at the pop-up mechanisms while opening and closing the book. They should notice that the pictures do not stick out when the book is closed. Finally, each group should find out whether all of the pop-up pictures in their book use the same kind of mechanism.

Task 4

Provide each group with a pop-up card. Ask them to take the card to pieces carefully and draw a diagram of the different parts — to show how the card was constructed. They could draw an exploded diagram. If the children have not already learned this technique, here is an excellent opportunity to teach them.

Task 5

Each group should now attempt to disassemble an envelope (of any type). They should be encouraged to note how many pieces there are, how it is folded and how it is stuck together. Then each child should draw a net of their group's envelope. Some children may need assistance with this task.

FOCUSED PRACTICAL TASKS

Materials/equipment needed: Copymasters 1, 2 and 110, paper, thin card, rulers, safety rulers, scissors, a perforator, a rotary wavy cutter, a rotary cutter, a compass cutter, pinking shears, PVA glue, glue spreaders, gluesticks, split pins, compasses, set squares.

Introductory tasks

Revise methods of cutting and tools used for cutting with, using Copymaster 110. Revise methods of marking out, cutting, and scoring card by working through the following tasks with the children. Check each individual's work carefully in order to assess their ability to measure and cut accurately.

Answers to Copymaster 110

Hand drill – *wheel (jelutong)*; scissors – *paper*; hacksaw – *jelutong*; strippers – *wire*; punch – *lollystick (correx, paper)*; stitch unpicker – *correx*; snips – *tubing (correx)*.

Marking out and cutting card

Take a thin piece of card. Demonstrate how to draw a rectangle on it — using a ruler and set square to mark out the shape accurately. (This provides a good opportunity to revise how to measure accurately from zero.) Then provide the children with pieces of thin card on which they should draw their own rectangles. Ask them to cut out their finished shapes using ordinary scissors. Before they begin, remind them how to use sharp tools, such as scissors, safely.

Using scraps of card, demonstrate other ways of cutting card. Show the children the effects that can be created by using pinking shears, a rotary wavy cutter, a rotary cutter and a compass cutter.

Scoring card

Revise how to hold a safety ruler. Emphasise that the children should always keep their fingers within the central groove. Then show them the correct way to score a straight line on a piece of card (Fig. 1, over the page), pointing out the way in which the card bends. Explain that this is why they should always score down the *outside* of a fold. (At this point, it might be worth reinforcing the idea that ordinary plastic or wooden rulers should not be used for this type of task, as their edges will become damaged.)

3

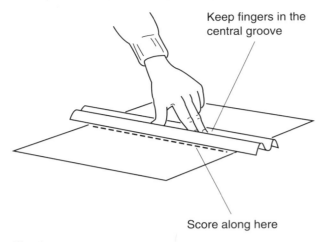

Keep fingers in the central groove

Score along here

Fig. 1

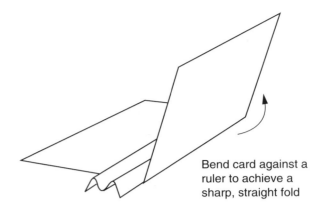

Bend card against a ruler to achieve a sharp, straight fold

Fig. 2

Encourage the children to apply this skill. Ask them to take the card rectangles they made for the first task in this section, and measure and make a mark halfway along each long side. They should then score a line to join the two marks, using a pair of scissors and a safety ruler. Ask them to bend the card against a ruler in order to make a straight fold along the scored line (Fig. 2). Then demonstrate that a perforator can also be used for scoring, and will break the surface of thick card, making it easier to bend.

Introduce the children to the idea that card can be scored to make tabs. Show them how to make a tab by scoring a line approximately 1 cm from the edge of a card rectangle. Then allow them to practise making their own tabs using scraps of card.

Independent task

Pop-up mechanisms
(In preparation for this task, make some of the card mechanisms shown in the sketches on page 5 — Fig. 3. Similar sketches also appear on Copymaster 1.) Provide the children with copies of Copymaster 1. Then show them the card mechanisms you have already made, and explain their construction. Challenge them to make two of these mechanisms using scraps of card and paper. They should use scissors and safety rulers for scoring, and gluesticks should be adequate for fixing thin card and paper. If thicker card is used, PVA glue is more suitable.

Making envelopes

Now, encourage the children to make an envelope for one of their cards, by following the instructions on Copymaster 2. These suggest that the children only make one of the designs shown on the sheet. However, you could make up both designs for them to examine before they begin this task (see Fig. 4). The only materials required for this activity are paper and gluesticks.

DESIGN AND MAKE ASSIGNMENT

Aim: To design and make a pop-up Christmas card. (Alternatively, the children could design and make a card for another religious festival or a more general occasion.)

Materials/equipment needed: Copymasters 1, 2, 3, 88 and 89, thin card, PVA glue, glue spreaders, paper, gluesticks, scissors, rulers, set squares, compasses, safety rulers, pinking shears, a wavy cutter, a perforator, split pins, felt pens, colouring pencils, sequins, glitter.

Introduction

The focused practical tasks (pages 3–4) should be used to introduce this project. After this work has been completed, challenge the children to make a pop-up Christmas card. However, before they design their cards, hold a general discussion about the nature of this task. Remind them of the different pop-up mechanisms that could be used. Also, explain that their product must be of a good quality, and that this will be evaluated at the end of the project.

Designing

Ask the children to sketch two or three Christmas-card designs. (Copymaster 3 could be used as a source of ideas.) They should then select one to develop. Encourage them to choose the design that will be the easiest to make (and therefore probably the most effective), rather than one which is too difficult to make (with the possibility of a poor result). They should draw an enlarged version of this design, which has details about colour and decoration marked on it. It should also have labels that describe how the pop-up mechanism is to be made, as on Copymaster 1.

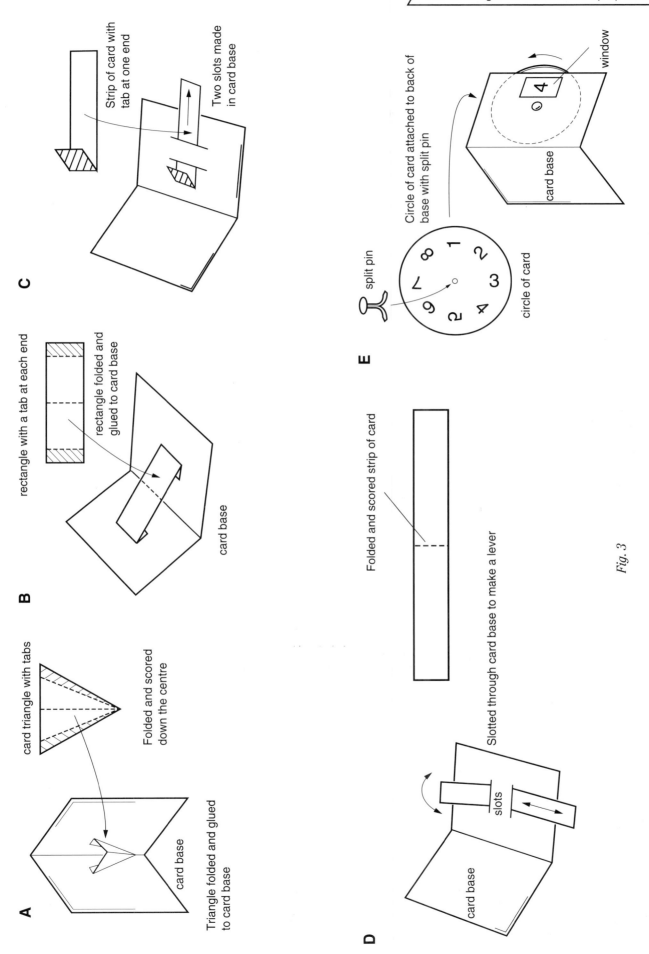

A

card triangle with tabs

Folded and scored down the centre

Triangle folded and glued to card base

card base

B

rectangle with a tab at each end

rectangle folded and glued to card base

card base

C

Strip of card with tab at one end

Two slots made in card base

D

Folded and scored strip of card

Slotted through card base to make a lever

slots

card base

E

split pin

circle of card

Circle of card attached to back of base with split pin

window

card base

Fig. 3

5

Design 1

1. Draw a rectangle 1 cm bigger than the card.
2. Measure and draw the centre lines (x and y).
3. Add a triangle to each side, as shown.
4. Cut out the shape.
5. Fold where the dotted lines are marked below.
6. Glue all the flaps except for A.

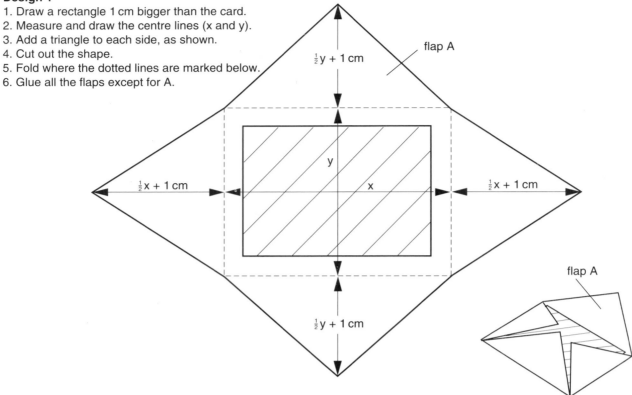

Design 2

1. Draw a rectangle 1 cm bigger than the card.
2. Measure the height of the rectangle (x).
3. Add a rectangle to each side, as shown.
4. Cut out the shape.
5. Fold where the dotted lines are marked below.
6. Glue all the flaps except for A.

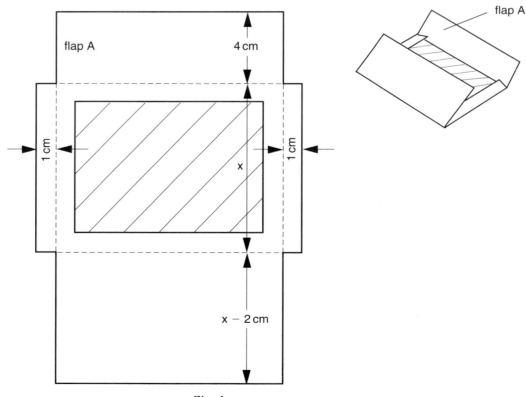

Fig. 4

The next stage involves the children modelling their ideas using paper. They should do this to check that their mechanism works and any pictures do not stick out when the card is closed. If necessary, adjustments can be made and noted on the final design. They should then write a step-by-step 'recipe' for making their card, and work out how their design can be translated on to card. Finally, they need to identify any parts of the mechanism that will need to be coloured, decorated, scored or stuck before the card is assembled.

Making

The making of the cards will be largely directed by the children, applying the knowledge they gained from the focused practical tasks. However, the stages in the making process are outlined below so that you can provide guidance where necessary. Before they start work, remind them how to use sharp tools safely. Also, encourage them to use materials economically, and stress that a good quality finish is required.

The children should translate their design on to card by drawing around or tracing their paper prototype. The components can then be coloured with felt pens or coloured pencils, cut out, scored and glued into position. Glitter, sticky labels, sequins, etc. can be added at this stage. Next, a message can be put inside the card.

The children should be encouraged to draft out their message in rough first. The final version could be typed on the computer, or printed using rubbed-down letters. If written by hand, the children could select a style of lettering from Copymaster 88 or 89 to reproduce. (Guidelines should be used for accuracy.) Finally, they should make an envelope from paper (white or coloured) using either of the designs shown on Copymaster 2.

Evaluating

The children should have the opportunity to evaluate their own and each other's cards. Discuss who each card might be for, how it works and whether it has a good quality finish. Then test whether it fits inside the envelope. Afterwards, display the cards in a prominent position in the classroom.

FOREX CLOCKS

Learning objectives

Designing skills

The children should be given the opportunity to:

- sketch a series of ideas, leading to a final design
- consider decoration, shape and colour
- design for a particular purpose.

Making skills

The children should practise:

- making templates from card
- cutting accurately with scissors
- using a shaper saw correctly
- achieving neat edges by using abrasive paper
- using adhesives and adhesive tapes correctly
- assembling a clock mechanism.

Knowledge and understanding

The children should learn:

- that forex is a manufactured sheet material which is waterproof and colourfast
- that forex can be easily cut and shaped to achieve a professional finish
- that care must be taken not to scratch the surface (unless this is done intentionally for the purpose of decoration)
- how to use a shaper saw safely.

Vocabulary: forex, shaper saw, template, sweep, portfolio.

INVESTIGATING TASKS

Materials/equipment needed: Copymaster 4; a collection of contemporary clocks; pictures of clocks and alternative devices for measuring time from different historical periods; an old clock.

Task 1
Display pictures of clocks and other devices for measuring time (e.g. a sundial or candle) from different historical periods. Encourage the children to research the development of clocks. They could then draw a timeline entitled 'Clocks through history'.

Task 2
Provide the children with a collection of contemporary clocks to examine. Ask them to draw and describe each one. They should then try to work out what each is used for, who might use it and where it would be situated, e.g. a digital timer in the kitchen and a carriage clock in the living-room.

Task 3
This activity could be used to assess the children's technical knowledge and revise basic vocabulary. Dismantle an old clock and discuss how it works. Then link this work to any relevant topics that have been studied in Maths and Science.

Task 4
The children should complete the comprehension exercise on Copymaster 4, which describes the development of clocks through history.

FOCUSED PRACTICAL TASKS

Materials/equipment needed: forex, shaper saws, safety-pins, masking tape, a plastic sheet cutter, a safety ruler, a craft knife, marker pens/overhead projector pens, goggles, double-sided sticky tape, sticky pads, a lino cutter, a pair of compasses, sandpaper, a file, sticky labels.

Introductory tasks
First, show the children a sheet of forex. Explain that this material is made of plastic, is waterproof and colourfast, and comes in a range of colours. Demonstrate that forex is slightly flexible.

Before starting these tasks, remind the children how to use sharp tools safely.

Cutting forex
Show the children this method of cutting forex. Score the forex using a plastic sheet cutter and safety ruler. Then 'snap' the sheet along the line. (This should be quite easy to do.)

This section focuses on how to teach the children to use a shaper saw to cut forex. First, show them ways of marking out a shape on a sheet of forex, by drawing on masking tape or using marker pens or overhead projector pens. Then cut out the shape using the shaper saw. Explain that the blade should not be pushed through the forex as it will bend and snap. Instead they should guide the forex gently in a forwards direction. (Remember to wear goggles for this demonstration.)

Joining forex
Demonstrate how to join pieces of forex using double-sided sticky tape or sticky pads. Hot glue is not so suitable for smooth plastics.

Scratching forex
Show the children how easy it is to scratch forex. This can be used to advantage, as a method of decoration. A pattern can be cut into the surface using a sharp tool, such as a lino cutter or even a pair of compasses.

However, reinforce the idea that the children should take care not to scratch this material unintentionally.

Achieving a good finish
Encourage the children to smooth the edges of cut forex using sandpaper. Show them how to use a file to shape the forex slightly.

Independent tasks
Working in groups of 4–5, the children should design a range of badges. These could be for a club, for the school (e.g. team badges) or linked to a particular theme. Emphasise the idea that their designs should be based on a simple shape, which can then be decorated.

After the task has been introduced, ask the group to sketch a series of badge designs. Each child should select one of these designs for development and draw a larger diagram of it. Then the design should be transferred on to a small piece of forex and cut out. (The cut edges of the forex should be finished neatly using sandpaper or a file.) The next stage is for the children to decorate their shapes with scratched patterns, sticky labels or permanent pens. Finally, a safety-pin should be attached to the back of each shape using a piece of masking tape, or for extra strength, an epoxy-based glue (Fig. 1).

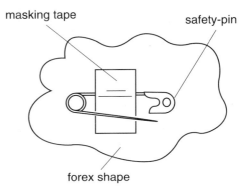

masking tape

safety-pin

forex shape

Fig. 1

DESIGN AND MAKE ASSIGNMENT

Aim: To design and make a forex clock for a room in your house.

Materials/equipment needed: Copymasters 5 and 6, forex (ideally pre-cut to 22 cm × 22 cm squares), safety rulers, thin card, scissors, masking tape, PVA glue, double-sided tape, sticky pads, clock mechanisms, shaper saws, spare blades, sandpaper/file, sticky labels, sequins, hand drill with 1 cm bit, pairs of compasses, squared paper, paper, overhead projector or marker pens.

Introduction

The Investigating tasks section (page 9) provides a general introduction to this project. However, it will be necessary to discuss the design brief (above) so that the children are aware of exactly what they are being asked to produce. Copymaster 5 could be used to support this discussion, as the children develop criteria for the project.

Designing

Provide the children with a clock mechanism (the same as those they will be using for their clocks) to examine, so that they are aware of how it fits together. Consolidate this knowledge by asking them to complete the exploded diagram of the mechanism on Copymaster 6. They should measure the length of the long hand and find the area of its sweep.

After the initial research, ask each child to sketch clock designs for a specific room or several different rooms. They can write any relevant notes alongside these designs. They should then select one design to develop and draw a larger sketch of it. Encourage the children to choose their simplest design, as this will probably be the easiest to make and the most successful. They should be made aware that they only have one large piece of forex (22 cm x 22 cm) with which to make their clock, and should therefore avoid unnecessary wastage.

The children should then consider how their clock faces will be decorated. Give them examples of the types of materials that could be used for decoration, e.g. small, shaped pieces of forex cut from scraps, sticky labels, sequins etc. Warn them that any decoration which gets in the way of the sweep of the hands will prevent the clock from functioning properly. Therefore, they should draw a circle on their design that indicates the area of the sweep of the hands and keep any decoration within it to a minimum (Fig. 2).

The next stage in this process involves the children drawing their design on to squared paper to the exact size. They should mark the area of the sweep of the hands and the centre point, where the hole for the spindle is to be drilled, on their drawing. (It would be a good idea for them to measure the brass spindle-fitting, in order to ensure that the hole is accurately drawn.)

Thick decoration, e.g. pieces of forex, should not be put in this area

Fig. 2

They should also annotate the diagram with notes on colour, decoration, etc.

Finally, individuals should write step-by-step plans or draw a flow diagram of how they intend to make their clocks. This exercise should clarify their thoughts and help them to organise their work better. (All of the children's sketches, designs, etc. could be retained and incorporated into a design portfolio.)

Making

First, the children need to trace the shape of their final design on to card to make a template. This should be cut out carefully and a spindle hole pierced through it. Then the shape has to be transferred on to the square of forex. As pen and pencil marks are not very visible on the surface of the forex, masking tape can be stuck on to the square and the outline drawn on this (Fig. 3). Alternatively, the shape can be marked out using overhead projector or marker pens.

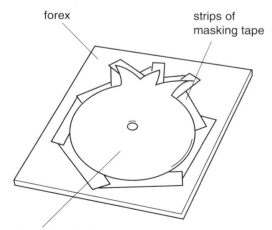

forex
strips of masking tape
Template with spindle hole cut out

Fig. 3

Each shape should then be cut out carefully using a shaper saw. Before the children begin this work, discuss how to use shaper saws safely, which includes wearing goggles. Also, remind them not to try and force the blade through the forex. Afterwards, they can finish the cut edges of their shapes using sandpaper or a file.

The next stage is to cut a hole for the spindle fitting. (This can be done using a hand drill with a 1 cm drill bit.) The hole needs to be large enough for the brass spindle-fitting to sit snugly inside. If necessary, the hole can be made larger using a circular file. Then the clock mechanism should be fitted, and any adjustments made before the clock face is decorated. (However, it is as well to remove the hands after the test as they are delicate and can be easily bent or broken.)

At this point, reinforce the idea that the children should keep to their original designs as far as possible, as this is an aspect of their work that will be evaluated. They should then proceed to finish their clocks. However, before they begin decorating them, explain that any pieces of forex to be used should be attached with double-sided sticky tape or sticky pads. This means that if mistakes are made, the tape can be removed without damaging the surface. If they wish to scratch a design on to the surface of the forex, this should be drawn on to masking tape first. When the decoration has been completed, the tape can be removed.

The final stages in the making process are for the hands to be replaced and a battery fitted to the back of the clock.

Evaluating
Ask each child to assess how closely their finished product resembles their design. Then test all the clocks. Afterwards, mount them on a wall together with the portfolio of designs. When the display is taken down, allow the children to take their clocks home. They should gain a great deal of satisfaction from showing others their work, especially if it is of a good quality.

UNIT 2:
FRAMEWORKS

A SHELTER FOR A CASTAWAY

Learning objectives

Designing skills
The children should be given the opportunity to:

- design using construction kits
- test different shapes for strength
- test simple structures for strength.

Making skills
The children should learn to:

- use construction kits to make simple structures
- make a stable framework
- choose suitable materials for a purpose
- use the triangle as the basis for a structure.

Knowledge and understanding
The children should learn that:

- triangles are strong
- that adding a diagonal to a shape, e.g. a square, will strengthen it
- different materials are suited to different purposes
- people build homes to suit their needs
- structures can have an external shell or an internal framework.

Vocabulary: triangle, diagonal, stable, strong, shell, framework, material, fabric, tube.

INVESTIGATING TASKS

Materials/equipment needed: Copymasters 7, 8 and 10; reference books that have pictures of houses from different historical periods and different parts of the world in them; building materials, including roofing materials.

Task 1

Initiate a discussion about homes. Ask the children why people build homes for themselves. Talk about the need for homes to be warm and dry, strong and safe. Then ask them to think of as many different types of home as they can, e.g. a castle, hut, house or house-boat. Their suggestions will probably include the types of homes in which they live. At this point, use Copymaster 7 to help the children identify different styles of home. Afterwards, ask them to bring in photographs of their homes for display.

Task 2

Talk about the materials that homes can be made of. If possible, provide the children with a collection of building materials to examine. (You may be able to acquire these free of charge from a local DIY merchant or friendly builder.) Then show them pictures of homes from the past or from other countries to identify the ways in which these materials can be used, e.g. timber-framed Tudor houses or contemporary Swedish homes made of wood.

Task 3

Talk about what types of materials are used for roofing. Then use Copymaster 10 to reinforce vocabulary. Afterwards, ask the children to find out what the roofs of their homes are made from.

Task 4

Explain that some people do not live in one place, but instead travel around taking their home with them. Show the children pictures of Bedouin tents, arctic explorers, travellers, canal barges, etc. and discuss them. Then reinforce the idea that, in general, building materials need to be waterproof and strong.

Task 5

Introduce the concept of structure by explaining that all objects have a structure, and this allows them to be the best shape for the job they do. Then develop this idea by asking the children to identify classroom objects that support themselves, i.e. 'hold themselves up'. Make a list of these things and their uses. Each child should then draw one of these objects and label its function and the material it is made of.

Task 6

Explain that objects can have their structure on the outside — a shell — or on the inside — a frame. Those with a shell normally hold something inside them. A frame supports the object from within. (Copymaster 8 can be used to reinforce this work.) Then make a collection of pictures that show structure and label the type of structure on each. Alternatively, the children could label the drawing they completed for Task 5 in a similar way, and draw in the structure using a coloured pencil.

Answers to Copymaster 8

skeleton – *framework*; tent – *framework*; jam jar – *shell*; snail – *shell*; cola can – *shell*; bridge – *framework*; pylon – *framework*; spider's web – *framework*; light bulb – *shell*; ladder – *framework*; cereal packet – *shell*; honeycomb – *framework*.

FOCUSED PRACTICAL TASKS

Materials/equipment needed: Copymasters 9, 108 and 109; construction kits, plastic geostrips, split pins, pencils, A4 paper, masking tape, hard-backed books, plastic containers, Ping-Pong® balls or similar, egg boxes, lengths of dowel, broadsheet newspapers.

Introductory tasks

Testing the strength of shapes

Provide the children with some plastic geostrips and split pins, and ask them to make a variety of shapes, including a square and a triangle. (This is a good opportunity to revise the names of the shapes.) Show them that when you 'push' one of the sides of a square it 'falls over' into a rhombus (Fig. 1). Therefore, this is not a very strong shape. Then repeat the demonstration using a triangle. The triangle does not collapse, and therefore is a strong shape (Fig. 2).

Challenge the children to think of a way to strengthen a square. Then demonstrate how a diagonal can be used for this purpose, pointing out how this splits the square

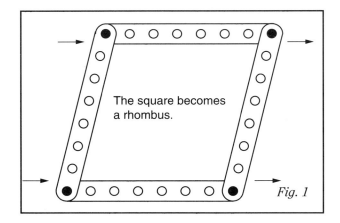

The square becomes a rhombus.

Fig. 1

into triangles. Reinforce this work by identifying the triangular structures of everyday objects.

Next, allow the children to use construction kits, such as Polydron, either in pairs or small groups, and ask them to make some solid shapes. Show them that a shape like a tetrahedron is very stable — because it is made entirely of triangles (Fig. 3).

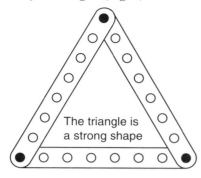

Fig. 2

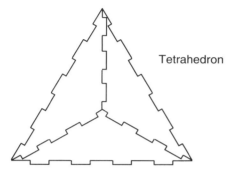

Tetrahedron

Fig. 3

Ways of joining shapes
Divide the class into small groups, and give each group a piece of A4 paper, a roll of masking tape and a pencil. Ask them to roll half the piece of paper around the pencil to make a tube. They should then secure the tube using masking tape. The other piece of paper should be folded in half.

Ask each group to stand their tube and piece of folded paper on the floor, and balance a hard-backed book on top of each in turn (Fig. 5). If the paper supports the weight of the book, a plastic container should be positioned on top. Then weights can be added gradually until the paper collapses. This experiment should show that a rolled piece of paper is much stronger than a single thickness. Demonstrate various methods of joining tube shapes, e.g. pipecleaners can be used to join drinking straws and

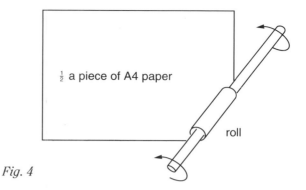

½ a piece of A4 paper

roll

Fig. 4

plastic tubing provides an effective way of linking pieces of dowel. (Copymasters 108 and 109 can be used to support this work.)

Answers to Copymaster 108
a) needle and thread; b) stapler (PVA or hot glue); c) gluestick; d) terminal block (circuit connector); e) drawing pins; f) PVA glue; g) Blu-tack®.

Independent tasks
Organise the children into groups of four or five, and give each group a broadsheet newspaper, a piece of dowel, a Ping-Pong® ball, a reel of masking tape and an egg-box section. Demonstrate how to roll newspaper around a piece of dowel diagonally — from corner to corner — and secure it using a piece of masking tape (Fig. 4). Then remind the children that tubes and triangles are strong shapes.

Next, challenge each group to build as high a tower as they can with a Ping-Pong® ball positioned on top of it. Explain that their structure must stand up on its own and hold the Ping-Pong® ball for at least 30 seconds. (Copymaster 9 can be used to give the children some criteria for their designs.) This activity should be carried out in a large space, such as the hall, and completed within a time limit. (With lower juniors, this task should take about an hour.) When the allotted time has expired, discuss each of the structures in terms of: height, strength, stability, appearance, economy, group co-operation, etc. Also, identify any triangular shapes in the structures.

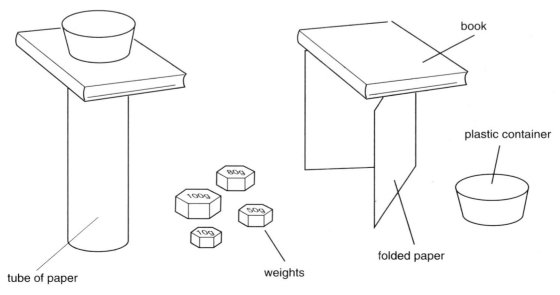

book

plastic container

Fig. 5   tube of paper

weights

folded paper

DESIGN AND MAKE ASSIGNMENTS

Aim: To design and make a shelter for a castaway.

Materials/equipment needed: Copymasters 11, 12 and 13; a miniature (e.g. Playmobil®) doll, construction kits, pipecleaners, drinking straws, fabric scraps, aluminium foil, cling film, string, scissors, wool, synthetic fur, PVA glue.

Introduction
Read aloud the poem on Copymaster 11 — 'Sailor Sam' by Sue Dillon. Then discuss what the children would do to survive on a desert island. They would definitely need to gather food, find water, make a shelter and send a distress signal. Provide them with copies of Copymasters 12 and 13 to locate suitable sites for doing these things, and to reinforce work on coordinates. Afterwards, give them Copymaster 11 to complete, and explain that they are going to make a shelter for a miniature doll.

The next stage is to show them the doll, so that they can judge the size of the shelter needed. Then recap the requirements of the shelter, i.e. that it is strong, warm and waterproof, and tell them their shelters will be evaluated against these criteria; reinforcing the concept of a design brief. Also, talk about the types of materials that could be used for building and covering shelters, ranging from reinforced concrete to wood, brick and animal skins.

Designing
The children should design their shelter using construction kits. (As there is often a lack of kit pieces to enable the whole class to work at once, it may be better to arrange the design work in stages, with a group of five or six children working at one time.) The framework could take the form of a cube, cuboid, triangular prism, or any other suitable 3D shape. Remind the group that triangles should be used to create a strong structure.

Once the children have constructed their shelter, they can then draw a diagram of it, adding on a cover.

Making
The shelter designs should now be modelled using alternative materials, e.g. pipecleaners and straws. Before the children begin this task, demonstrate how to link several straws at one point (Fig. 6). Also, show them how to join pipecleaners by, for example, twisting them into a 'Y' shape or hooking them together (Fig. 7).

Once the basic framework has been made, the children then need to cover it. They should, if possible, have access to a variety of materials for this purpose, ranging from aluminium foil and cling film to wool and synthetic fur. Using their knowledge of materials and the previous work done on homes, they should choose appropriate materials to make a cover that is warm and waterproof. The children should then be encouraged to measure the sides of their framework, and to cut pieces of their chosen material that are a little larger than the frame. The cover can be attached to the shelter in many ways, e.g. stitching, lacing, gluing, etc. The children

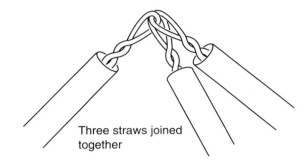

Three straws joined together

Fig. 6

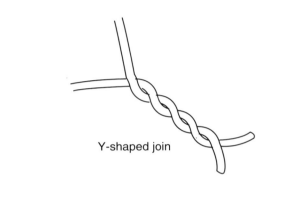

Y-shaped join

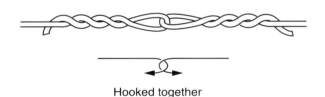

Hooked together

Fig. 7

should be left to choose their preferred method where practical. However, before they begin this task, teach them to fold the edges of the material around the frame in order to produce a neater finish. When attaching the cover, some children may remember to leave one end open for access, and may even consider a way to fasten the doorway. Others may prefer to focus their attention on a way to fix the shelter to the ground.

Evaluating
As shelters were to be designed for a miniature doll, the first method of evaluation is to test that a doll fits inside them. Next, the shelters should be tested to see if they are waterproof. This can be done spraying on water using a plant spray bottle. Those that resist the water can be commended. Finally, the design brief stated that the shelter had to be warm. Unfortunately, this cannot be readily tested, but those shelters that have thick walls and a thick floor or incorporate wool (or fur-type fabrics) and those with few gaps in the structure can be commended.

BRIDGES/ PLAYGROUND EQUIPMENT

Learning objectives

Designing skills
The children should be given the opportunity to:

● examine pictures of bridges from different historical periods
● use construction kits to model different types of bridges
● use paper to model and test a design
● incorporate 'strong shapes' into designs
● sketch several ideas, selecting one for development
● label diagrams of designs to show their purpose
● use isometric and squared paper for designing.

Making skills
The children should practise:

● the paper-rolling technique
● working as a team to fulfill specific design criteria

● using construction kits
● reinforcing structures using paper rolls, dowel and diagonals
● using reclaimed materials
● using adhesives appropriately
● achieving a good finish.

Knowledge and understanding
The children should learn that:

● there are five main types of bridge
● the arch and triangle are particularly strong shapes
● diagonals are useful for reinforcement
● structures need to be strong
● a good finish improves a product.

Vocabulary: structure, arch, triangle, diagonal, load, force, specifications, 'finish'.

INVESTIGATING TASKS

Materials/equipment needed: Copymasters 14 and 15, card, weights, hard-backed books, reference books about bridges.

Task 1
Make a timeline of bridges through history that includes: a tree-trunk across a stream, a rope bridge, a clapper bridge (as in Dartmoor), the Egyptian arch bridge, a Roman aqueduct, an arch bridge with buildings on it (e.g. Ponte Vecchio, Florence), an opening bridge (e.g. Tower Bridge) a drawbridge, a canal swing bridge, an iron bridge (e.g. Brunel's bridge at Ironbridge), a suspension bridge (e.g. Telford's Menai Straits bridge and Fairburn's tubular Britannia bridge), a cantilever bridge (e.g. the Firth of Forth bridge) and a concrete bridge (e.g. Salginatobel in Switzerland and Waterloo Bridge in London). Display it. Then ask the children to complete Copymaster 14, using the timeline for reference. (The answers are: 1 clapper; 2 rope; 3 arch aqueduct; 4 cantilever; 5 suspension; steel arch.)

Task 2
Carry out this experiment to determine whether arch bridges are stronger than beam bridges. First, use a piece of card and some books to make a beam bridge (Fig. 1). Start placing weights on the bridge. Continue adding more until it collapses. Add two books to the ends of the card to hold it down (Fig. 2), and add weights in the same way as before. You should find that this bridge is stronger. Then construct an arch bridge (Fig. 3). (The strip of curved card rests on the lower books). Determine its strength. Change the design of the bridge by anchoring the card strip at each end with a book (Fig. 4), and test its strength. Then discuss your findings as a group.

Task 3
Copy the diagrams of the five main types of bridge: beam, arch, suspension, cantilever and cable-stayed (Figs 5-9). (The arrows indicate in which directions forces act upon these structures.) Then show them to the children and describe each bridge's characteristics, using the text below for reference. Afterwards, individuals can complete Copymaster 15 to consolidate this knowledge.

A beam bridge
This structure consists of a rigid beam supported by a series of pillars, anchored at each end to the ground or piers. Any weight in the middle of the beam tends to bend it downwards, making this type of bridge unsuitable for longer distances.

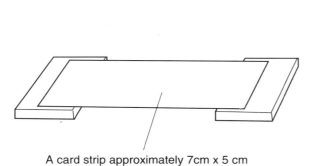

A card strip approximately 7cm x 5 cm

Fig. 1

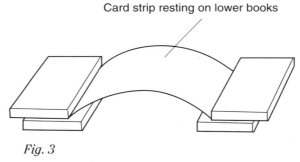

Card strip resting on lower books

Fig. 3

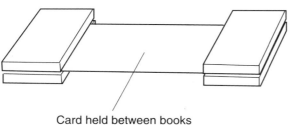

Card held between books

Fig. 2

Card strip anchored down by books

Fig. 4

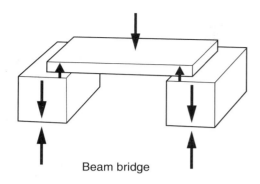

Beam bridge

Fig. 5

An arch bridge

The weight is carried outwards along curved paths. The ground resists this outwards force, keeping the bridge up. A road can go across the top of an arched bridge or through it.

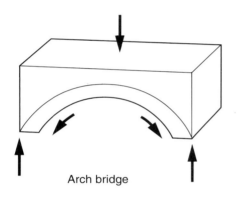

Arch bridge

Fig. 6

A suspension bridge

The roadway is supported by cables that are anchored at each end of the bridge. The cables take the weight to the top of the towers, which transfer the force downwards to the ground. Modern cables are made of strands of steel wire that only stretch under excessive weights. This makes the suspension bridge suitable for long spans.

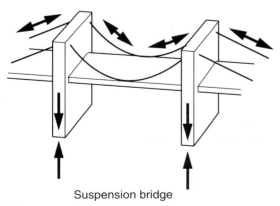

Suspension bridge

Fig. 7

A cantilever bridge

The ends of the bridge are weighted sufficiently to be able to carry a central beam between them. The end beams are built out from the banks that are to be joined by the bridge, and a smaller beam joins the two ends together.

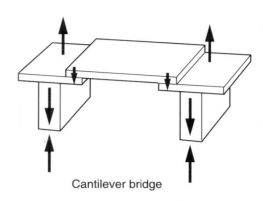

Cantilever bridge

Fig.8

A cable-stayed bridge

This is a new development in bridge technology. There may be one or two towers built in the centre of the deck, and the roadway is supported by cables that are directly connected to these. As this type of bridge requires few piers, it is increasingly used for wider rivers and estuaries.

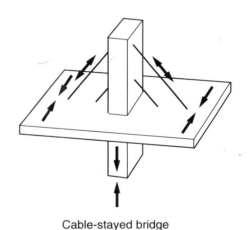

Cable-stayed bridge

Fig.9

Task 4

Using a suitable construction kit, the children should be encouraged to model one of the types of bridge described above.

FOCUSED PRACTICAL TASKS

Materials/equipment needed: newspaper, lengths of dowel, masking tape, geostrips, split pins, thin card, squared/isometric paper, heavy books, a metre rule, toy trucks.

Introductory tasks

Testing the strength of shapes
This task can be used to revise earlier work that related to shapes and their relative strengths. Use geostrips and split pins to make a triangle and a square. Demonstrate that a square is not a strong shape, and will 'fall over' into a rhombus when one side is 'pushed'. Then show the children that when a triangle is placed under a similar amount of pressure it does not collapse, and is therefore a much a stronger shape. Ask them to suggest ways of making the square stronger, i.e. by adding a diagonal (Fig. 10).

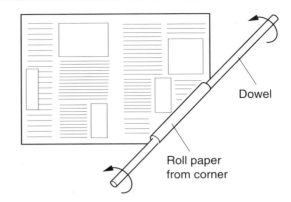

Dowel

Roll paper from corner

Fig. 11

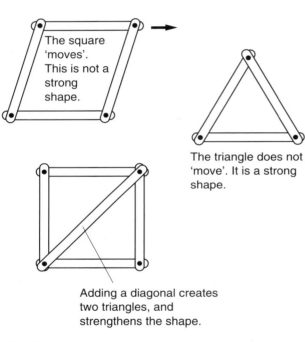

The square 'moves'. This is not a strong shape.

The triangle does not 'move'. It is a strong shape.

Adding a diagonal creates two triangles, and strengthens the shape.

Fig. 10

Making structures from rolls of paper
Demonstrate the technique used for rolling paper. Take a sheet of newspaper and place a length of dowel across the corner of it. Roll the newspaper around the dowel and secure it using masking tape (Fig. 11). Then proceed to slip the dowel out of the centre of the roll, and fold it approximately 5 cm from the each end.

Make several paper rolls in this way, and show the children how to tape them together to make fairly strong structures such as a triangle (Fig. 12), rhombus and tetrahedron, or tape rows of triangles together to make a grid (Fig. 13). Sheets of card can be used to fill the holes in the framework. Then ask each child to make a paper roll in preparation for the next task.

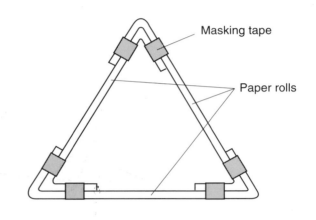

Masking tape

Paper rolls

Fig. 12

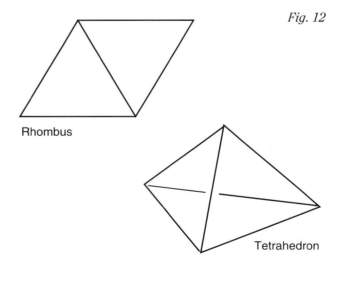

Rhombus

Tetrahedron

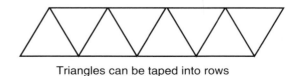

Triangles can be taped into rows

Fig. 13

20

Independent tasks

This activity should be carried out in a large space, e.g. a hall, and should take approximately an hour to complete. First, divide the class into groups of four to six. Challenge each group to design and make a bridge that will span a 1 m gap between two tables and hold a toy truck. Then provide the children with squared or isometric paper on which to draw their bridge design, and explain that they will have the following materials to work with: sheets of newspaper, thin card, masking tape and a few lengths of dowel. Also, emphasise that they should make their bridge using the techniques outlined above, and it may be weighted at each end with just one heavy book.

As the groups begin to construct their bridges, encourage them to use strong shapes and to reinforce these with diagonals where necessary (Fig. 14). Different groups will probably have different methods of working; some may even organise themselves into a production line. Each way of approaching this task should be pointed out to the rest of the class, and its advantages and disadvantages discussed.

When the children have used up all the time available, the bridges should be tested — using two tables as supports and a metre rule to check the distance. The bridge is successful only if it holds one truck without collapsing. Any signs of bending should be noted! Afterwards those bridges that have proved successful can be further tested by either adding more trucks or weights.

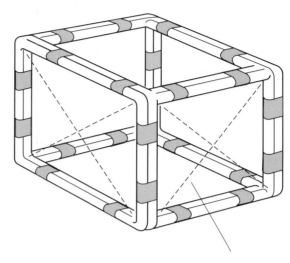

Diagonals are needed to make this shape stable

Fig. 14

DESIGN AND MAKE ASSIGNMENT

Aim: To design and make a piece of equipment for a children's playground.

Materials/equipment needed: Copymasters 16 and 17, plain newsprint (or newspapers), masking tape, thick card or wooden bases, thick string, lollysticks, pipecleaners, reclaimed materials, poster paint, scissors, lengths of 3.5 mm dowel, squared/isometric paper, PVA glue, plastic tubing, sticky pads, emulsion, model paints, wire wool/sandpaper.

Introduction

Provide the children with Copymaster 16 — a mock newspaper cutting that details the outcome of a public meeting, held to decide the fate of a disused plot of land in the local area. Explain that following this meeting, the local council has been persuaded to allocate this piece of land as a children's play area, and have consequently set up a survey to find out what children require and want before having any equipment designed. Then tell the children that they are going to help with this project by designing and making a piece of playground equipment.

At this point, you might like to decide on a theme for the equipment. Alternatively, the children could choose their own. Then discuss what they think the purpose of the equipment should be and what age groups would use it. Also, remind them of the types of equipment that are in most playgrounds, e.g. climbing frames, swings, seesaws. Do these encourage children to use lots of different skills, e.g. climbing, crawling, etc? If not, members of the group could adapt the designs so that they do.

After the initial discussion, explain that the council requires sketches of the ideas that the children have for different pieces of equipment, and each child will need to model at least one of their designs. Emphasise that the models should be strong and stable, based on a theme and have a definite colour scheme.

Designing

This is a good opportunity for the children to brainstorm lots of ideas and then choose one to develop. Before they select a design to model, ask them to sketch ideas for five or six different pieces of playground equipment using squared or isometric paper. They should have access to library books to help gain information about possible shapes, and themes, e.g. animals and outer space. Also, a visit to a local play area could be arranged. The sketches of equipment should then be labelled to show what activities they would be used for, e.g. rolling and climbing. The age group that the equipment has been designed for should be indicated, together with the theme that is being followed and the colour scheme. Then remind the children of the paper-rolling technique described earlier, and reinforce ideas about strong shapes, etc. They should also be aware of the different materials

21

available for this project. The next stage is for individuals to select the design they are going to develop. Ask them to produce a large drawing of it, detailing the materials to be used and how it is to be constructed. Copymaster 17 should be used to support this work.

Making

Provide the children with several sheets of paper, a length of 3.5 mm dowel and access to a reel of masking tape. Encourage them to follow their diagrams in order to construct the basic frames for their apparatus. They should begin this process by making several paper rolls and cutting these into small pieces — each approximately 1/3 of the total length. As they model the apparatus, they could reinforce the frames with additional rolls and diagonals of paper. If necessary, they could be shown how to strengthen these frames by leaving short lengths of dowel inside the paper rolls (Fig. 15).

Once the frames are complete, the children can add accessories using reclaimed materials, e.g. lollysticks, pipecleaners, string, beads, dowel, etc. Suggest that they join dowel using plastic tubing to give their work a good finish. Plastic tubing can also be used to stop pipe cleaners from sliding off (Fig. 16). These can be attached with masking tape or preferably PVA glue. Then the structures should be attached to strong bases using sticky pads or tape, and painted with liquid poster paint. If plastic components have been used, e.g. yoghurt pots, the surface of these should be roughened using wire wool or sandpaper and painted with white emulsion (which hides the lettering). Afterwards, they can be painted with poster paint. To achieve a glossy effect, a coat of clear varnish can be added.

Evaluating

The best way to evaluate each piece of work is to display the original working drawing with the detailed drawing, alongside the model created, and assess their similarity.

Reinforcement:

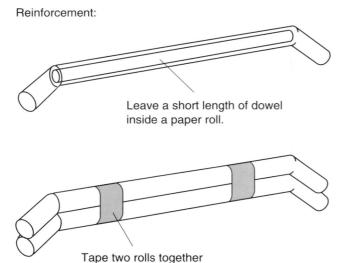

Leave a short length of dowel inside a paper roll.

Tape two rolls together

Fig. 15

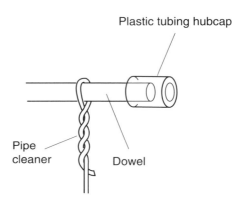

Plastic tubing hubcap

Pipe cleaner

Dowel

Fig. 16

UNIT 3:
MOULDABLE
MATERIALS

CHRISTMAS DECORATIONS

Learning objectives

Designing skills
The children should be given the opportunity to:

- design a shape that can be moulded
- create a design that can be repeated several times
- include textures into the moulded material.

Making skills
The children should practise:

- moulding materials into different shapes using different techniques
- using tools and equipment safely
- using tools to create patterns and textures.

Knowledge and understanding
The children should learn that:

- some materials can be moulded
- the substance to be moulded can be changed from a pliable material into one that is rigid and hard.

Vocabulary: clay, slab, wedging, mould, shape, pliable, rigid, coil pot, slab pot, pinch pot.

INVESTIGATING TASKS

Materials/equipment needed: Copymaster 18, pieces of soft and fired clay; a collection of, and pictures of, moulded objects and moulds.

NB: Please note that although the clay recommended for the following activities needs to be fired in a kiln, it can be substituted with self-hardening clay, Fimo® or salt dough. Self-hardening clay is quite an expensive alternative, which can be baked in the oven to harden it further and should be painted according to the makers' instructions. Fimo® is also quite expensive, but comes in vivid colours and is easy to use. Furthermore, it can be baked in an oven according to the manufacturer's instructions and varnished to achieve a good finish. Salt dough is by far the cheapest alternative, and can be made from equal measures of flour and salt, mixed together with a little water. This is a very malleable substance, but is not so easy to make lasting impressions on. It should be slowly baked in the oven at a low temperature. Then it can be painted with poster paints before varnishing with several coats of model varnish.

If you are using a kiln to fire clay, follow the manufacturer's instructions carefully.

Task 1
Discuss some different ways of shaping materials, e.g. cutting, folding, drilling, carving, rolling, moulding, etc. Then ask for suggestions as to which materials could be shaped, or moulded. Explain the difference between shaping a material by hand and pressing it into a mould.

Task 2
Make a collection of objects, and pictures of objects, that have been moulded in one way or another. The collection should include clay objects, injection moulded plastics, cast iron, pastry cases and chocolate bars. Also, try to bring in a variety of types of mould that the children should be familiar with, e.g. jelly moulds, cake tins, paper cake cases, lolly moulds. The children should be made aware that moulding is a very commonly used process.

Task 3
Talk about the changes that take place in materials when they are dried and fired. Then provide the children with pieces of unfired and fired clay, and ask them to make a comparison. They should notice that the soft, malleable clay becomes hard and brittle when it is fired. This change is permanent.

Task 4
Point out that other materials melt when heated, e.g. chocolate becomes runny and ice cubes turn into water. Do the children think these changes are permanent or not?

Task 5
Provide each child with a clay object and ask them to write a description of it using Copymaster 18.

FOCUSED PRACTICAL TASKS

Materials/equipment needed: clay, clay slip (shreds of clay mixed with water to make a paste), pottery tools, hessian pieces, yoghurt pots, brooch backs (available from craft shops), biscuit cutters, epoxy glue, under-glaze, stains, oxides, transparent glaze, round magnets.

Introductory tasks
These tasks are designed to teach the children how to prepare and use clay. However, they can be adapted if an alternative mouldable material is to be used.

Removing air bubbles
Provide each child with a piece of clay and a square of absorbent material, e.g. hessian, to work on. Show them how to prepare, or 'wedge', the clay by kneading it in the same way as bread dough would be kneaded (Fig. 1). Then the clay should be rolled into a ball and cut in half to check for air bubbles (Fig. 2). (It is important that all the air is removed from the clay before it is fired, as this may cause it to explode.) Aterwards, the two halves should be banged together (Fig. 3) and the clay kneaded again, until all of the air bubbles have been removed.

Making a pinch pot
Show the children how to roll the clay into a ball and, using their thumbs, make a pinch pot (Fig. 4). Squeeze the walls of the pot from the bottom outwards while turning it in the palm of your hand.

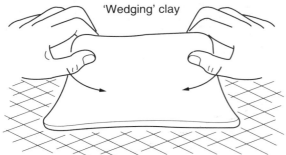

'Wedging' clay

Push the clay inwards and away from you.

Fig. 1a

Prepare the clay on a hessian mat.

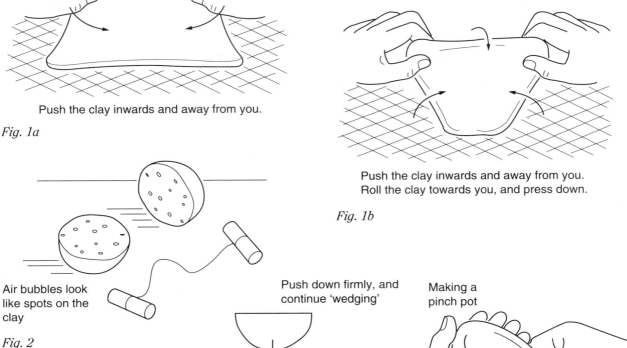

Push the clay inwards and away from you.
Roll the clay towards you, and press down.

Fig. 1b

Air bubbles look like spots on the clay

Fig. 2

Push down firmly, and continue 'wedging'

Fig. 3

Making a pinch pot

Cup the pot in one hand

Squeeze walls from the bottom outwards

Fig. 4

Rolling out and cutting clay

In preparation for this task, either give each child another piece of clay or ask them to collapse their pinch pot and knead the clay out again. First, demonstrate how to flatten a lump of clay with your hands. (Use a square of hessian to prevent the clay from sticking to your working surface.) Then show the children how to roll out the lump using a rolling pin (Fig. 5). After rolling out the clay in one direction, it should be lifted and turned. Remember to point out that the rolling pins in use are different from those used for food technology!

Next, give each child a yoghurt pot and a knife. Ask them to place the pot on the clay and cut around it to make a base (Fig. 6).

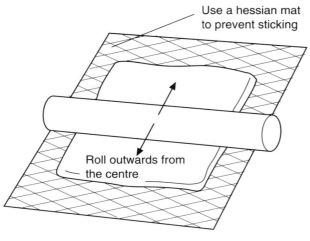

Use a hessian mat to prevent sticking

Roll outwards from the centre

Fig. 5

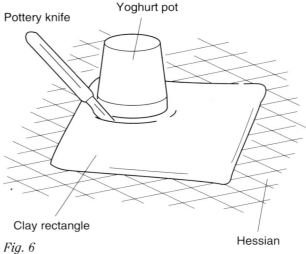

Pottery knife

Yoghurt pot

Clay rectangle

Hessian

Fig. 6

Making coil pots

Demonstrate how to roll a coil of clay, from the centre outwards. This should be fixed to a base (made previously) with slip, and pressed down (Fig. 7). Further coils of clay can then be stuck on using clay slip, making sure that the ends of the coils meet in a different place each time. Each coil should be joined to the previous one using the fingertips. To finish the pot, smooth the surfaces with your fingertips so that all traces of the coils disappear (Fig. 8).

Base

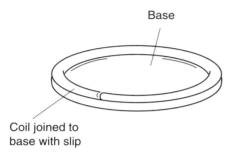

Coil joined to
base with slip

Fig. 7

Coils joined at different places

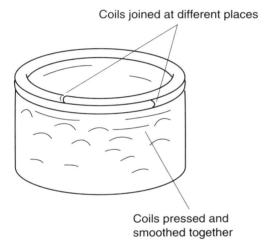

Fig. 8

Coils pressed and
smoothed together

Making slab pots

Ask the children to roll out a rectangle of clay. This should be left for a day to go leather-hard, which will make it easier to handle. Then rectangles should be cut from the slab using a knife (Fig 9). These could be joined together with slip, brushed along their edges, to make a box (Fig. 10).

Slip should also be brushed along each join, and a sausage of clay added to strengthen it. Finally, the joints should be smoothed with a wooden tool, filling in any gaps with more clay (Fig. 11).

Independent tasks

Explain that the children are going to make a brooch or a fridge magnet. Ask them to roll out a slab of clay about 3 mm thick. They should then cut a shape into the clay using a knife or, for a more intricate shape, they could use a small biscuit cutter (Fig. 12). This shape should be smoothed along the edges with a damp sponge, and then can be decorated using under-glazes (which can come in pens or tubes) or stains and oxides. Under-

glazes can also be used on biscuit-fired clay. (For details of firing, see the manufacturer's manual for your particular kiln.) The shape should then be painted with a coat of transparent glaze. Finally a brooch-back or round magnet should be stuck to the back of it using an epoxy-type glue. This task may have to be completed by an adult, without children present, if fumes are likely to cause a problem (Fig. 13).

Cut rectangles out of clay slab

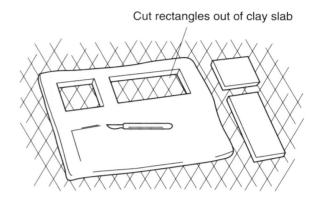

Fig. 9

Slide pieces across the base
until they stick

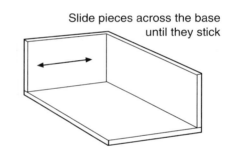

Fig. 10

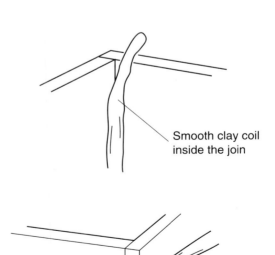

Smooth clay coil
inside the join

Use a wooden tool to
smooth outside of join

Fig. 11

27

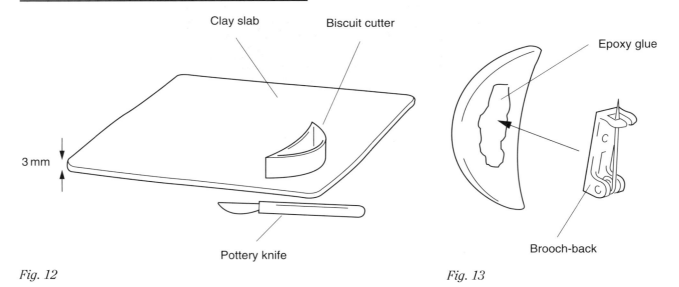

Clay slab

Biscuit cutter

Epoxy glue

3 mm

Pottery knife

Brooch-back

Fig. 12

Fig. 13

DESIGN AND MAKE ASSIGNMENT

Aim: To design and make a set of three similarly shaped Christmas decorations to hang on a Christmas tree.

Materials/equipment needed: Copymasters 19, 106 and 107; clay, pottery tools, glazes, biscuit cutters, card, paper, felt pens, ribbons/glittery thread, knitting needles/hole cutters, under-glazes, stains, model varnish.

Introduction
Discuss the work done previously using mouldable materials and the techniques learned. Then outline the task and identify the key requirements that the finished products will need to fulfill. For example: ' the decorations need to hang from the tree, they should be carefully made and finished, and attractive to look at. Also emphasise that the children's designs must be easy to make, as they have to make three similar decorations. This could lead to a discussion of the benefits of using press moulds, such as biscuit cutters, to cut shapes. Then revise the process used to make the badge or fridge magnet. Also at this point, mention that each decoration will need to have a hole in the top (made with a knitting needle) so that it can be attached to the tree by a ribbon or piece of thread.

Designing
Ask the children to bring in some decorations from home. They should examine these to see what each is made of, how it is decorated and how it hangs. Then use Copymaster 19 to develop some design criteria. Afterwards, ask the children to sketch their initial ideas. They should choose one to develop further. This should ideally be a flat shape, so that it can be easily repeated. (Flat shapes also have the advantage of being easier to fire, as they take up less room in the kiln.)

The next stage is for the children to model their design in paper or card, using the appropriate biscuit cutter if possible. If cutters are not available, they could make a template to cut around. The card model should then be coloured and decorated. At this point, it may be worth reminding the group that decoration on clay should be kept simple.

Finally, the children should design a flow diagram to show the stages in the making process, using Copymaster 106. If necessary, remind them that they will need to make a hole in the top of their shapes for attaching string.

Making
The children should roll out a piece of clay to a thickness of about 3-5 mm. They should then cut out three identical shapes using their biscuit cutter or template as a guide. A hole can be made in each with a knitting needle or a hole cutter, and patterns scratched and marked on them with pottery tools (these need not be identical on all of the shapes). The shapes can then be painted, using under-glazes or stains, before being fired. (As before, the decoration does not need to be consistent.) The fired clay pieces should be coated with a transparent glaze before being fired again, and finally, a piece of ribbon or glittery thread can be looped through the hole in the top of each.

NB: If salt dough is being used the making process is the almost the same, but rather than glazing the shapes, they can be baked and then painted. The final products should then be varnished, with a model varnish, before adding threads or ribbons.

Evaluating
The children should be able to evaluate their own work using Copymaster 107. They should also review their flow diagram to see whether any changes could be made. Finally, the decorations should be hung on a Christmas tree — either at school or at home.

UNIT 4:
TEXTILES

WALL-HANGINGS

Learning objectives

Designing skills
The children should be given the opportunity to:

- model ideas using paper
- design paper patterns
- consider appearance of their products.

Making skills
The children should practise:

- making a simple paper pattern
- cutting through several thicknesses of fabric
- pinning a paper pattern to fabric, and fabric to fabric
- joining fabrics using a variety of stitches
- joining fabrics with the right sides together using textile tools.

Knowledge and understanding
The children should learn that:

- some fabrics are more suited to a specific purpose than others
- patterns can be used in a number of ways
- careful pattern-laying can minimise wastage
- laying a pattern on a fold will produce a mirror image.

Vocabulary: fabric, colour, texture, thickness, pattern, natural, man-made, binka, stitches, running stitch, soldier stitch, cross stitch, back stitch, oversew, needle, thread, pin, lining, template, pattern pieces, hessian, hem, right sides, wrong side.

INVESTIGATING TASKS

Materials/equipment needed: Copymasters 20, 21 and 22; fabric scraps, magnifying glasses, plastic containers, weights, sandpaper/a nail, a hairbrush/comb, a pipette.

Introductory tasks
These tasks could be linked to topic work on materials.

Task 1
Divide the class into groups, and give each group a collection of fabric scraps — consisting of at least ten different types of material. Ask them to sort the scraps into sets. When they have done this, ask each group to explain what criteria they used for sorting their collection. They will probably have used the following criteria: colour, texture and thickness.

Task 2
Provide the children with a piece of fabric each. They should be encouraged to describe it in terms of colour, pattern, thickness and texture, and record this information on Copymaster 20. They could also use a magnifying glass to study its appearance more closely, and decide whether it has been woven or knitted (Fig. 1).

Using Copymaster 21 ask the children to state whether certain materials originate from animals, plants or minerals.

Answers to Copymaster 21

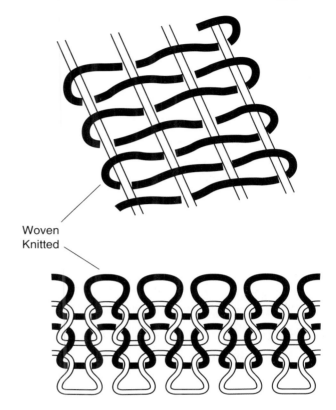

Woven
Knitted

Fig. 1

Where do textiles come from?			
Cotton	Plant	grown in warm, moist regions of the world	used to make all kinds of clothes
Lycra	Mineral	made from fossil fuels	used to make stretchy clothes
Wool	Animal	comes from sheep, goats, camels, llamas all over the world	used for carpets, clothes, felt and upholstery
Kapok	Plant	grown in Java, Indonesia and southern parts of Asia	used as stuffing in upholstery and cushions
Fur	Animal	comes from the skin of animals all over the world, particularly mink, seal, deer, ermine	used mainly for clothing
Nylon	Mineral	made from fossil fuels such as oil	mostly used for carpets and clothes
Rubber	Plant	made from the sap of the rubber tree grown in India and southern Asia	used mainly for footwear
Acrylic	Mineral	made from fossil fuels	used for making clothes
Suede	Animal	made from the hides mainly cattle and goats	mostly used for footwear, clothes and accessories
Hessian	Plant	made from the *jute* plant grown in tropical regions such as India and Pakistan	used for sacking
Felt	Animal	made from wet woollen fibres compressed together and shrunk	used for craft activities, tennis balls and some clothing
Polyester	Mineral	made from fossil fuels	used for making clothes
Leather	Animal	made from the hides of animals especially cattle and goats	used for clothing, footwear and accessories
Silk	Animal	made from the cocoons of the silk worm in Japan, China, India, Mexico and Turkey	used for stockings, dresses, blouses and underwear

Task 3
The children could test the strength of their piece of fabric by hooking a container, e.g. a margarine tub, to the end of some strips of the fabric and adding on weights. They could test for abrasion, by rubbing each of the strips 50–100 times with a piece of sandpaper or a nail. They could also test for fraying, by pulling at the edges of a strip with a hairbrush or comb. Finally, they could investigate their fabric's waterproof qualities/absorbency by putting five drops of water on to the fabric, using a pipette, and measuring the size of patch produced.

Task 4
Encourage the children to suggest what their fabric could be used for, and where it would be used, e.g. a shiny fabric could be made into a dress to be worn at a party and towelling could be used to make a bathrobe. Alternatively, this activity could take the form of a quiz, with groups guessing the function of a range of fabrics. Copymaster 22 should be used to supplement this task.

Task 5
Explain that some materials are naturally produced while others are manufactured from minerals, e.g. polyester is made from oil. Then identify any school clothes or objects that are made from a combination of materials. Copymaster 21 could be used to reinforce this work.

FOCUSED PRACTICAL TASKS

Materials/equipment needed: Copymasters 23 and 24, binka (five holes per inch), embroidery threads, textile tools, remnants of cotton fabric, Velcro/poppers.

Independent tasks

This activity teaches the children how to make and decorate a pencil case using several different stitching techniques. These techniques are described in detail on Copymasters 23 and 24.

Provide each of the children with a rectangle of binka 34 cm × 27 cm (67 × 54 holes). Ask them to count in four holes all the way round and mark this border with a pencil line. Then, if necessary, teach them how to thread a needle, and fasten the end of the thread — by making a couple of small stitches on the back of their binka (Fig. 2). Discourage them from making a knot.

On the opposite side of the binka to the pencil line, the children should make a border of running stitches six rows from each edge (Fig. 3). They should then use a different-coloured thread to make a second border one row inside the first. This second row of stitches should alternate with the first (Fig. 4).

Next, demonstrate how to weave a zigzag stitch through the two rows of running stitch, making a daisy pattern at each corner (Fig. 5). The children should then do the same using a third colour. Afterwards, show them how to sew another border, using a soldier stitch, one row in from the last border. The children should copy this using a fourth colour (Fig. 6). The final row comprises double-cross stitches that form stars. As before, this should be stitched one row inside the last border using another coloured thread (Fig. 7). This should leave a rectangle of 24 × 36 holes without any stitching on it in the middle of the binka.

The next stage is to show the children how to fold under the short edges of the binka using the pencil line as a guide. These should be pinned securely. The binka must then be folded in three, like an envelope (Fig. 8). Ask the children to turn over the envelope and pencil their initials in the space on the back. They need to make sure that the envelope is the correct way up and the initials

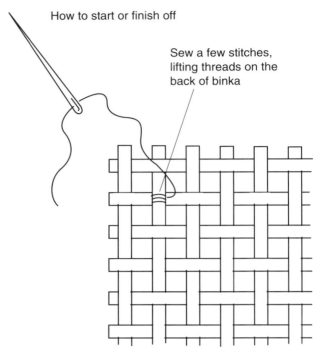

How to start or finish off

Sew a few stitches, lifting threads on the back of binka

Fig. 2

follow the lines of holes, where possible (Fig. 9). The initials should then be sewn using backstitch.

The children should now begin to attach the lining of the pencil case, made from a rectangle of cotton fabric the same size as the binka. The binka and cotton lining need to be placed right sides together and pinned. Then three of the sides should be sewn together (using backstitch) following the pencil line. The bottom edge must be left open (Fig. 10). When the pencil case is turned right sides out, this can be pinned and oversewn.

Next, ask the children to refold the pencil case into its envelope shape, checking that the initials are the right way up and the oversewn end is on the inside. The envelope should then be pinned into position and the sides oversewn (Fig. 11).

Finally, Velcro or poppers can be stuck or stitched on to the pencil case to fasten it.

Edge

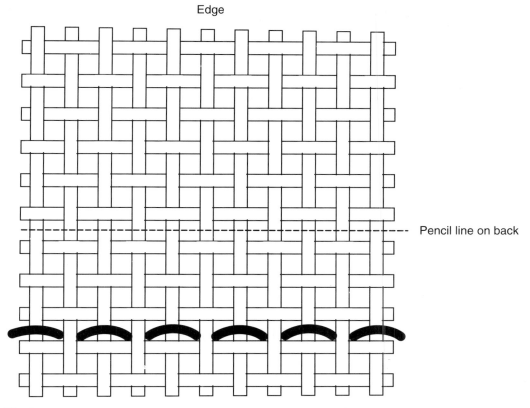

Pencil line on back

Fig. 3

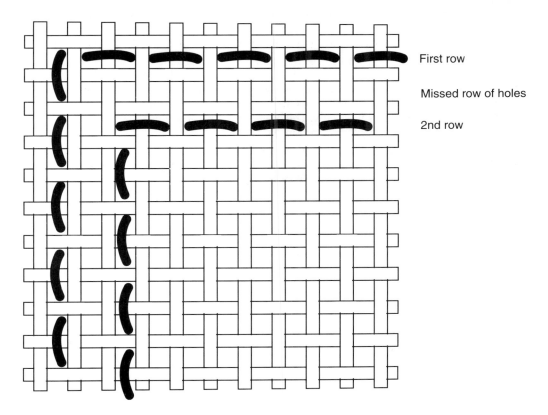

First row

Missed row of holes

2nd row

Fig. 4

Daisý pattern at corner

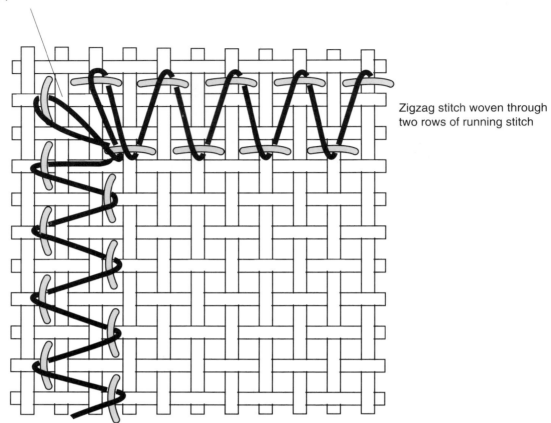

Zigzag stitch woven through
two rows of running stitch

Fig. 5

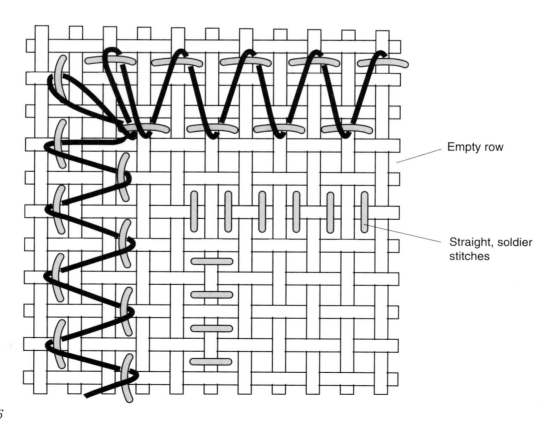

Empty row

Straight, soldier
stitches

Fig. 6

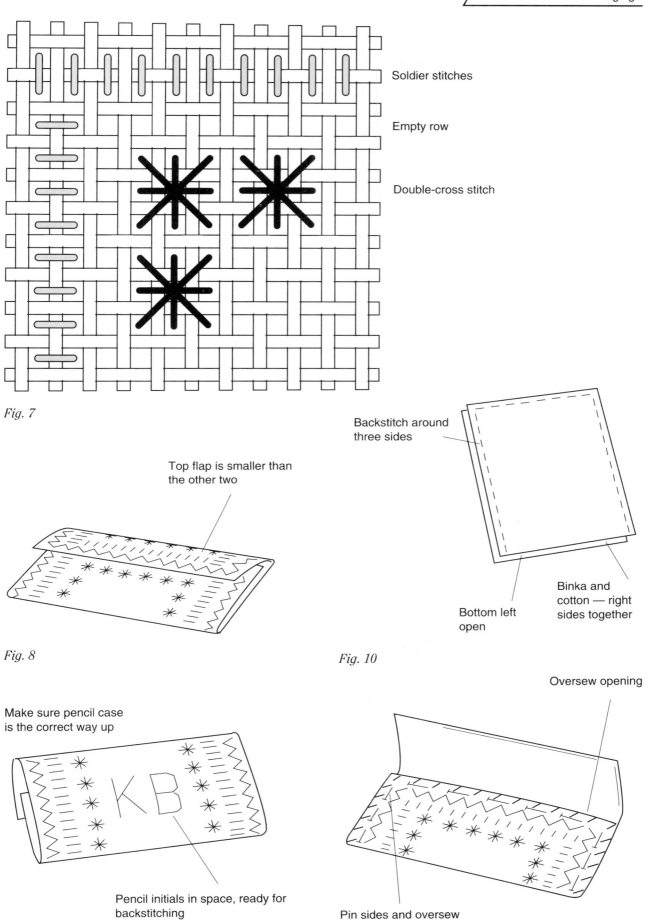

Soldier stitches

Empty row

Double-cross stitch

Fig. 7

Top flap is smaller than
the other two

Fig. 8

Backstitch around
three sides

Bottom left
open

Binka and
cotton — right
sides together

Fig. 10

Make sure pencil case
is the correct way up

Pencil initials in space, ready for
backstitching

Fig. 9

Oversew opening

Pin sides and oversew

Fig. 11

DESIGN AND MAKE ASSIGNMENT

Aim: To design and make a wall-hanging for your bedroom.

Materials/equipment needed: Copymaster 25, A4 squared paper, drawing equipment, crayons, rectangles of hessian (25cm × 37.5cm), fabric scraps, ribbon, braid, beads, embroidery thread, needles, scissors, pins, pinking shears, dowel, string, hacksaws, bench hooks, PVA glue, an iron and ironing board.

Introduction

Tell the children what they are going to make, and if possible have a ready-made example to show them. Explain that they will be using the skills they have already learned to stitch and join fabrics. Also emphasise that, for simplicity, their wall-hangings should be made up of geometric shapes, i.e. squares, circles, rectangles, etc. (They could be decorated e.g. with ribbons, braids and beads.) Then ask the children to think carefully about where their wall-hanging will hang and the colours in that area. They should aim to match the colour scheme of their wall-hanging to its surroundings. Copymaster 25 could provide a useful starting point to this work.

Designing

Provide each of the children with a piece of squared paper on which to design their wall-hanging. Suggest that they create a picture or an abstract design to provide decoration. Also explain that if they wish to add ribbon or braid, they should leave a 1cm border around the edge of their design. Emphasise that they should keep their designs simple, rather than adding too many details which they will be unable to reproduce. They can then draw and colour in their design, using plain colours only.

When the designs are complete, give the children another piece of squared paper each to draw out their patterns. They should draw out all the different shapes that make up their design without overlapping them in any way. There needs to be enough room to draw in a 1cm hem around each. Then tell them to colour each piece appropriately and write 'cut 2' or 'cut 3' on shapes that are repeated.

The next stage is to draw in the 1cm hem around the shapes. The patterns can then be cut out. Encourage each child to check their pattern by laying out all the shapes and comparing the overall effect to the original design.

Making

First, give each a child piece of hessian, and ask them to draw a line 4cm from one end using a pencil and ruler. (This is to allow room for the hessian to be attached to the piece of dowel.) They should then draw another line, approximately 2cm in from the edge, all the way round. This creates a border inside which the A4-sized design will be placed (Fig. 12).

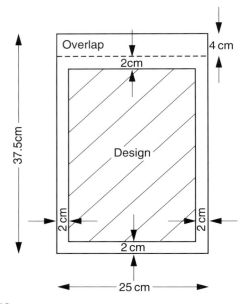

Fig. 12

The next stage in the making process is for the children to select the fabric scraps they wish to use. These should be as close as possible in colour to the original design; but patterned pieces can be substituted where the base colour is the same. Then the patterns should be pinned to the pieces of fabric and cut out. Emphasise that shapes should be pinned securely at the edges of the fabric in order to minimise wastage. Also, encourage the children to cut out two shapes together where possible. Once all of the fabric shapes have been cut out, they can be pinned to the hessian. The children should try to arrange them in the same way as is shown on their design. They can then begin to sew the pieces to the hessian, using some of the decorative stitches learned earlier. If the pins are not sufficiently secure, the shapes can be stuck down using PVA glue and sewn around the edges for decoration. When all of the pieces are in place and the pins removed, the braid or ribbon can be sewn around the border (if desired). Alternatively, running stitch can be sewn around the pencil-line border. If any beads are to be added, this should be done next. The next stage in the process is to attach the wall-hanging to the dowel. First, measure, mark and cut a piece of dowel 29cm long. Then the 4cm turning at one end of the hessian can be folded over it. The raw edge can either be trimmed with pinking shears or turned under (Fig. 13) and the hem pinned securely and sewn with a hem stitch.

Finally, the wall-hanging can be ironed (if necessary), and string should be tied around each edge of the dowel to create a hanger (Fig. 14).

Evaluating

The best way of evaluating these wall-hangings is to hang them in the places they were designed for, i.e. the children's bedrooms. However, before the children take their work home, it should be displayed alongside their designs. The pattern pieces can be retained for assessment purposes.

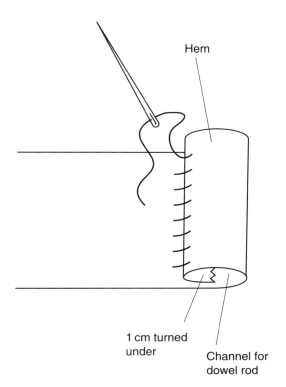

Hem

1 cm turned under

Channel for dowel rod

Fig. 13

Tie string around the dowel

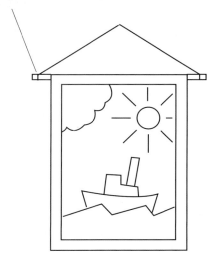

Fig. 14

FABRIC-COVERED BOXES

Learning objectives

Designing skills
The children should be encouraged to:

- consider the user of a product
- think about the appearance and function of products
- think about fabric design
- use isometric paper for designing
- draw annotated diagrams showing measurements
- design a box appropriately sized for its intended contents
- design and make pattern pieces.

Making skills
The children should practise:

- measuring and cutting accurately
- making identically-sized 3D frames with right-angle corners
- using a junior hacksaw and a bench hook

- drawing, making and using pattern pieces
- pinning and cutting fabric pieces correctly
- covering card with fabric and joining fabrics together creating a padded surface
- making a hinge and a fastening for the box
- achieving a neat finish to the edges of the box.

Knowledge and understanding
The children should be given the opportunity to:

- relate different containers to their uses and users
- examine different types of fastening and hinges
- investigate how containers are constructed
- identify frame structures
- choose suitable materials for covering, padding, hinging and fastening a box.

Vocabulary: container, user, function, three-dimensional (3D), fastening, hinge, uprights, pattern, turning, fray, covering, lining, wadding, padding, quilting.

INVESTIGATING TASKS

Materials/equipment needed: Copymasters 26 and 27, a collection of different types of containers, isometric paper, cardboard boxes.

Task 1

Ask the children to bring in some containers from home. (These could range from cereal packets to sponge bags.) One at a time, individuals should hold up a container, and the rest of the class must suggest what it is for and who might use it. Then select some of the more elaborate ones and discuss their decoration. Ask the group why they have been designed in this way and who they are intended for. Afterwards, use Copymaster 26 to encourage the children to make a more detailed examination of one container.

Task 2

Discuss 'traditional' and stereotypical designs, e.g. a jewellery box with a ballerina for young girls, a Paisley-printed sponge bag for men and a floral tissue box for women. Encourage the children to try to find containers that break with these 'traditions'.

Task 3

Now, ask the children to examine the fastenings of some of the containers they have brought from home. They should draw or list as many different types as they can. These may range from a simple card flap as on a cereal packet to a metal lock on a jewellery box. They should then investigate hinges in the same way.

Task 4

Give each child a cardboard box, and ask them to take it apart carefully. They should then look at the way in which it has been constructed. Next, obtain an old, unwanted, wooden box and take this apart, pointing out the differences between it and a cardboard box. Discuss how its frame has been constructed and how the covering is attached. Using isometric paper, the children could draw a diagram of the box, showing its construction. This is an excellent opportunity to teach them how to use isometric paper, as for this task they will be drawing mainly cuboids.

Task 5

The following task can be linked to maths work that involves the investigation of nets. Using Copymaster 27, the children should find as many shapes as possible that incorporate six squares. The squares must touch at the edges, not corner to corner or half overlapping (Fig. 1).

Answers to Copymaster 27

1. Already given

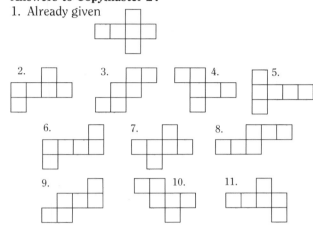

Then, working in groups, they should try to discover which of these shapes will make cubes when cut out and folded. Collectively, they could produce a poster that shows all eleven possibilities.

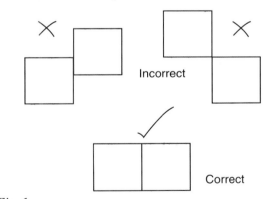

Fig. 1

FOCUSED PRACTICAL TASKS

Materials/equipment needed: Copymasters 28, 29, 30, 31, 32 and 33; ramin/jelutong, card triangles, PVA glue, gluesticks, hot glue-guns, rulers, scissors, bench hooks, junior hacksaws, laminated centimetre-squared mats, squared paper, squared card, braid, wrapping paper, pieces of fabric, coloured gift tape, masking tape, beads, ribbon, correx scraps, thread, buttons.

Introductory tasks

Making a wooden frame

The purpose of this task is to teach the children how to make a 3D frame. It is assumed that they are already capable of making a 2D frame, and so if this technique has not yet been covered, it would be advisable to work through the Focused practical tasks in the 2D chassis section (page 79). However, even if the children have practised making this type of frame, it would be worth revising the skill.

(Use Copymaster 28 to assist the teaching of this task.) First, for speed and ease, copy the triangles on Copymaster 29 on to thin card. Also make copies of Copymaster 30. Then explain to the children that they are going to make two frames. For simplicity, specify that the longer sides should be 15cm and the shorter ones 5cm, as in the 2D frame. Also, stress that the frames must be identical. They should then proceed to make two 2D frames.

When the 2D frames are complete, the children need to fold the large triangles in half, and stick them in position on the corners of the two frames using PVA glue (Fig 1). They must then cut eight lengths of wood, each exactly 5cm long. These will be used to make the uprights. PVA glue should be spread on the insides of the corners and the uprights stuck in position with hot glue while the PVA dries (Fig. 2). When the glue is dry, the children should add a 2D frame to the top of each structure using the same method (Fig. 3).

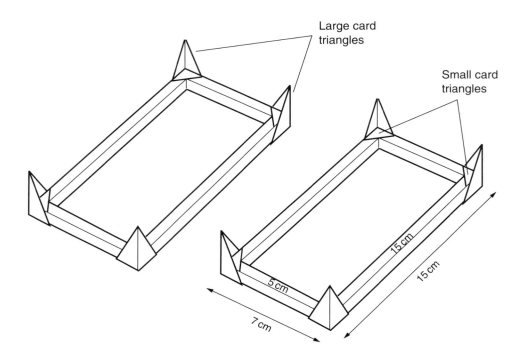

Fig. 1

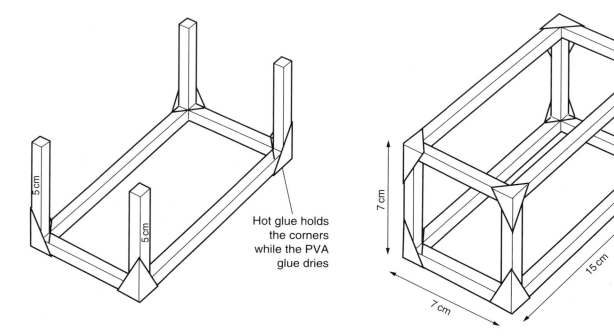

Fig. 2

Fig. 3

40

Covering the frame
(Copymaster 32 can be used to assist the teaching of this stage.) Once the frames are dry, show the children how to cover them. (This provides a good opportunity to revise the method for making a pattern.) Initially, the task should take the form of a demonstration, but, if time allows, each child could work through the whole process. This will help them to complete the design and make assignment successfully.

First, draw five rectangles on a piece of card. Three of these should be 15cm × 7cm (for the front, back and bottom of the frame), and two should be 7cm × 7cm (for the sides). These will make the sides of the box. (If the children attempt this activity, they could be given centimetre-squared card to use. This will assist accuracy, and the squares will not show as they will be covered later on.) Then cut out the rectangles and draw around each one on to squared paper or card, adding a centimetre border (Fig. 4). When the pattern is transferred on to fabric or paper, this will allow you room to turn under the edges of the material.

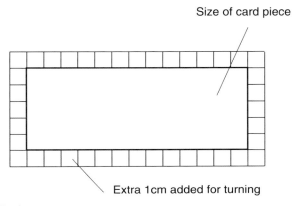

Size of card piece

Extra 1cm added for turning

Fig.4

The next stage is to attach the pattern to the covering (either fabric or paper), cut it out and attach the card rectangles in position. (If using wrapping paper, they can be stuck centrally on the paper using a glue-stick.) It may be helpful to measure and mark the 1cm turning, to ensure correct positioning. Then show the children how to snip across the corners and fold in the sides of each one (Fig. 5).

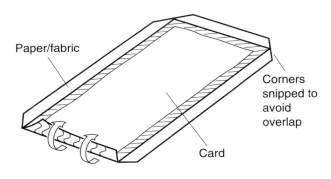

Paper/fabric

Corners snipped to avoid overlap

Card

Turn ends in and glue

Fig. 5

Provide the children with a similar box that has a lid. Point out that the lid is made from another 2D frame, and is attached so that it can be opened. Then demonstrate the different ways of making hinges and fastenings (Fig. 6). Copymaster 31 illustrates these techniques. (If you are making a masking-tape hinge for your box, the lid should be attached before the card pieces are stuck to the frame, thereby covering the tape.)

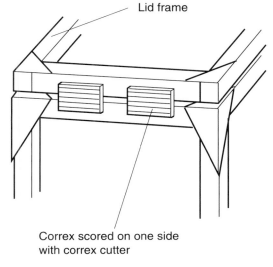

Lid frame

Correx scored on one side with correx cutter

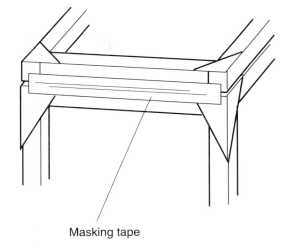

Masking tape

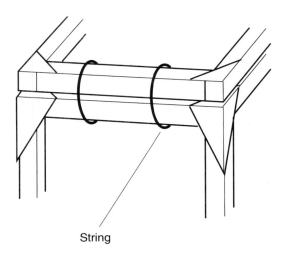

String

Fig. 6

Afterwards, using a thin layer of PVA glue, the covered card pieces can be stuck to the wooden frame. To cover the joins, use masking tape, coloured gift tape or braid glued with PVA. For economy, strips of the same wrapping paper/fabric can be cut and pasted over the edges (Fig. 7).

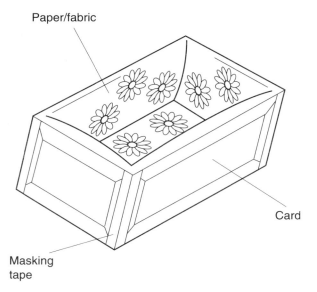

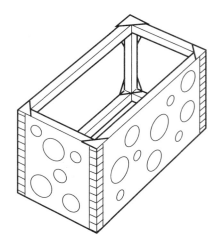

Fig. 7

Making a lining for the box
Use Copymaster 33 to assist the teaching of this task. The simplest way to line the inside of the box is to cut pieces of card or paper 2cm smaller than the exterior size of the box, i.e. three pieces 13cm x 5cm and two of 5cm × 5cm. These can then be fixed in position using a gluestick. A more professional way is to use the same technique practised earlier. Cut a piece of card for the base, 13cm × 5cm, and cover it in the same way as before. This should then be glued to the interior of the base with PVA glue. Next, cut four pieces of card the same height as the box but 2cm narrower, i.e. two pieces 7cm × 5cm and two 7cm × 13cm. These can also be covered in the same way, turning the edges of the fabric/paper underneath. Explain that some padding could be incorporated into the lining of the box. This is simply done by cutting wadding rectangles a little smaller that the card rectangles cut for the lining. The padding is then placed between the fabric or paper and card before the edges are turned over (Fig. 9). Join them

Fig. 8

with masking tape, in a strip, with the covered side inwards (Fig. 8). The strip should then be slipped inside the box and glued to the wood struts using PVA or hot glue. Finally, the wood rim around the top of the box can be covered with ribbon or braid, or simply painted carefully.

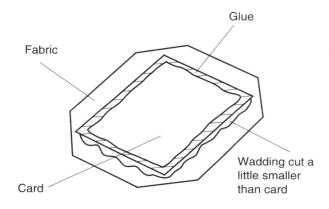

Fig. 9

DESIGN AND MAKE ASSIGNMENT

Aim: To design and make a fabric-covered box for a specific purpose.

Materials/equipment needed: Copymasters 28, 29, 30, 31, 32, 33 and 34; ramin/jelutong, bench hooks, junior hacksaws, card triangles, PVA glue, gluesticks, hot glue-guns, paper, fabric scissors, squared paper, card, isometric paper, laminated centimetre-squared mats, braid, fabric pieces, wadding, ribbon, beads, buttons, correx scraps, masking tape, thread, needles, needlework pins.

Introduction
Initially, simply summarise the work the children have already completed in this section. Then explain that they are going to make a fabric-covered box for a particular purpose, e.g. a pencil box, a jewellery box, a stationery box or a money box. (Copymaster 34 could be used to prompt ideas.) Tell them that the fabric can be on the inside or outside of the box. Also, emphasise that they must decide on the function of their box before they make it, and stick to this decision throughout the project.

Designing

The children should begin by drawing a diagram of the box they are going to make. (They could use isometric paper to help to get the perspective right.) The purpose and user of the box must be indicated on the drawing. Then ask them to annotate their picture to show the size of the box. To do this accurately, they will need to acquire examples of the types of items that will be put in the box — most children find it impossible to guess measurements. Next, encourage them to think about how their box will be decorated. Allow them some time to collect and store fabric pieces that they want to use. They should indicate on their diagram how the box is to be decorated and whether it should be padded. The children can then design patterns and templates, as for previous activities in this section.

Making

(Copymasters 28-33 should be used to support this task.) The making process should follow the stages outlined in Focused practical tasks (pages 39–42). As the children will be using fabrics, they may need assistance with pinning, cutting and any stitching techniques that they employ when decorating the box.

Evaluating

The design brief stated that the box should be used for a particular purpose. The best method of testing this is to fill it with the articles it was designed to hold. Also, it could be assessed whether a suitable fabric has been chosen for the covering. Afterwards, the children's work should be displayed.

UNIT 5: FOOD

CHUNKY FRUIT FOOL

Learning objectives

Designing skills
The children should be given the opportunity to:

- use different ingredients to produce different flavours
- find out about personal preferences
- adapt a simple recipe.

Making skills
The children should learn:

- to use food technology tools safely
- to cut and combine different fruits
- different whisking techniques.

Knowledge and understanding
The children should learn that:

- different fruits produce different flavours
- there are many varieties of fruit which are available at different times of the year
- food must be prepared hygienically
- safety rules should be followed carefully.

Vocabulary: whisk, knife, mix, chop, slice, peel, product, flavour, colour, texture, variety, make, weigh, grammes, litres, hygiene, menu, preference.

45

INVESTIGATING TASKS

Materials/equipment needed: Copymasters 35, 36 and 98; a range of different flavours and makes of yoghurt, spoons, plates, drawing equipment.

As the following tasks involve tasting foods, parents should be informed as to the nature of this work in advance. (Copymaster 98 could be used for this purpose.) Any child who is deemed to be unable to taste the foods should work with a partner and rely on their results.

Task 1

(Copymaster 35 should be used to support this activity.) Divide the class into groups, and give each group a set of yoghurts consisting of different flavours in unmarked pots. Ask each child to predict which their favourite flavour will be. Each member of a group should then taste every flavour. At this point reinforce aspects of food hygiene, i.e. the children in each group should not use the same spoon, but instead have one set of spoons in the various pots, which should be used to transfer the yoghurt on to a plate, and another set of spoons for tasting the yoghurts.

After the tasting, each child should decide which flavour yoghurt they liked best and record this, and the choices of the other members of their group, on Copymaster 35. These results can be then collated and translated into the form of a table or graph. Then they could be combined to create a class survey.

Task 2

Each group should then be given a set of yoghurts, again in unmarked pots, that are all the same flavour, but are different makes from different shops. Ask them what they expect from each product, i.e. what it should taste like. They need to think of at least four criteria, which will probably include creaminess, flavour and thickness. Each group should then test their set of yoghurts and give each product a mark out of five for each criteria. Provide them with Copymaster 36 to record the scores. These can be added up to identify a favourite product. Next, the price of each product needs to be found out in order to make a judgement as to which is the best value for money, taking into account the price and the flavour.

Afterwards, the groups' results can be compared. However, if the different groups are all testing different flavours, a comparison should be made to see if one particular brand comes out the best overall.

FOCUSED PRACTICAL TASKS

Materials/equipment needed: Copymasters 37, 38, 39, 40 and 41; different types of fruit, especially unusual types and those that are in season; food technology tools, small knives, cutting boards.

Food hygiene

When the children are introduced to food technology, and at intervals after that, all aspects of hygiene should be covered in detail. Teach them always to wear an apron and to tie long hair back. They should also be taught to wash their hands when handling food and to remember not to touch their face or hair, or to put their fingers in their mouths. If they do, their hands must be washed again. Discourage them from mixing art equipment with food equipment, and reinforce the idea that food ingredients and tools should be kept separately from other resources. They should be taught to clean up carefully, wiping up any spills, and putting waste in a closed, lined bin (if possible). A working surface should be cleaned with an anti-bacterial detergent before and after use.

Copymaster 37 can be used to teach aspects of food hygiene. The children have to label and colour the poster, and give it a suitable title.

Safety

Food technology safety rules should also be taught. Emphasise that the children should not use the cooker or sharp tools unless an adult is present. Also, they should wear oven gloves when handling anything hot, and hot pans should be placed on a heat-proof surface, away from the edge, with their handles turned to the side. The children need to take particular care when using sharp knives. Finally, any puddles or spills should be wiped up immediately to prevent the floor becoming slippery.

Copymaster 38 can be used to reinforce food technology safety rules.

Equipment

The children should be taught the names of the food technology tools that they will commonly use, and a quick outline of their uses can be given. Copymasters 39 and 40 could then be used to revise this information. Once the general ground rules for preparing and handling food have been established, the children can proceed to complete the Focused practical tasks.

Independent tasks

The children should work in groups to carry out the following tasks. Each group should be given a similar collection of fruits. Then individuals can select one of the fruits to investigate. They should take note of the characteristics of its skin, i.e. its colour, texture, and whether it is edible or not. (This information should be discovered by asking rather than tasting!) If the skin is edible, the child should cut off a piece carefully and taste it, noting its thickness. Then indentify those fruits that should be peeled, and show how this can be achieved using the appropriate tools.

Next, under close supervision, the children should cut their fruits up and describe the insides. Ask them to note down their colour and the amount of the juice, the texture of the flesh and whether any stone or pips are visible. Having found out all they can about the appearance of the fruit, they should be able to try a small piece of each one. Copymaster 41 can be used to record their findings. Then demonstrate how to prepare each fruit, and describe its most common uses. Finally, the children in each group should decide which is their favourite fruit and record these results.

DESIGN AND MAKE ASSIGNMENT

Aim: To design and make a new type of fruit dessert.

Materials/equipment needed: Copymasters 42, 43, 99 and 100; fruit-flavoured yoghurts, caster sugar, fruit of various types, decoration, e.g. chocolate buttons, wafers; small knives, peelers, chopping boards, medium-sized bowls, different types of whisk, dessert dishes, tablespoons, kitchen scales, serving bowls.

Introduction
First, review the work completed for Investigating tasks and Focused practical tasks. Then provide each child with a copy of the menu shown on Copymaster 42. Explain that although the dessert called 'Chunky Fruit Fool' appears on the menu, the chef isn't quite sure what recipe to use to make it. He wants to make a dessert that appeals to children as well as adults, but needs some ideas as to popular flavours etc. Then tell the children that they are going to make a 'prototype' dessert for the chef by adapting a recipe, so that it contains a palatable blend of fruit flavours.

Designing
Provide each child with a copy of Copymaster 43, which has the same recipe as below printed on it. Ask them to adapt the recipe by writing in the flavour of yoghurt and type of fruit they would like to use to make their dessert. They could use a fruit and yoghurt that have the same flavour, but ideally they will choose to use an appealing combination, e.g. blackberry and apple!

Recipe for 'Chunky Fruit Fool'
Ingredients
150g fruit yoghurt
25g caster sugar
110g fruit
wafer biscuits, fruit pieces and chocolate buttons for decoration

Equipment
small knife
chopping board
medium bowl
whisk
tablespoon
kitchen scales
serving bowls

Method
1. Peel and chop the fruit into small pieces. Put some pieces aside for decoration.
2. Put the yoghurt into a small bowl, and whisk until thick and creamy.
3. Add sugar to the yoghurt, and whisk it again.
4. Add the fruit to your mixture, and stir it in.
5. Pour the mixture into serving dishes, and decorate with the saved fruit pieces, chocolate buttons and biscuits.
6. Chill before serving.

The children should compose a shopping list of all the ingredients they will need. Then either the school can supply them, and ask for a voluntary contribution from the parents to cover the cost, or the children can be asked to bring in ingredients from home. The method of obtaining ingredients should be decided upon before asking for parents' permission for the children to embark upon this work. Then according to the decision, individuals can either complete and take home Copymaster 99 or 100.

Making
Divide the class into groups of six to eight. Once this has been done, the groups can begin to make their desserts, using Copymaster 43 for reference. Encourage them to measure out their own ingredients to the nearest 25g/25ml. Also, remind them of the correct way to use a knife when cutting the fruit, and teach them how to use a whisk properly. This would be a good opportunity to show the children the different types of whisk available, ranging from hand and balloon whisks to rotary whisks. Electric whisks and liquidisers can be demonstrated, although it is not necessary to use these for this project.

Evaluating
The best means of evaluating the desserts is to eat them. This can be done at lunch-time, or later in the classroom. If the tasting is done in the classroom, the children can try different versions of the recipe, describe their taste and choose their favourite. If there is time, the children should draw a picture of their product on Copymaster 42 before it is eaten. They should then write a description of it, on the menu card, to entice people to choose it. This task reinforces the use of descriptive language and persuasive writing.

PIZZA PICNIC

Learning objectives

Designing skills

The children should be given the opportunity to:

- select foods to create a range of balanced meals
- design a healthy meal
- consider the preferences of another person when designing
- consider taste, colour, texture and appearance in order to produce an attractive display
- investigate the packaging of particular types of food.

Making skills

The children should practise:

- measuring and weighing ingredients accurately following a recipe independently
- mixing and combining foods
- using basic tools/equipment correctly
- following food hygiene rules
- using a cooker for boiling and baking, under supervision.

Knowledge and understanding

The children should learn:

- to follow basic hygiene rules
- to identify the different parts of the cooker and understand what they are used for
- that food must be stored carefully to keep it fresh and safe
- that foods contain different nutritional elements
- that they need a balanced diet to be healthy
- how the characteristics of foods change when they are mixed, cooked etc.

Vocabulary: diet, nutrition, balanced, proteins, carbohydrates, starches, sugars, fibre, fats, minerals, vitamins, hob, grill, oven, refrigerate, hygiene, rubbing in.

INVESTIGATING TASKS

Materials/equipment needed: Copymasters 44, 45, 46, 47 and 48; kitchen tools, a cooker, a fridge, a microwave.

Task 1

Provide the children with copies of Copymaster 44, and ask them to identify the kitchen tools from their silhouettes. (They should be given assistance with spellings where necessary.) Then check their work and discuss any mistakes that have been made. To extend this activity, ask the children to describe, in a sentence, what each piece of equipment is used for.

Task 2

(Before starting this task, reinforce the idea that individuals should only use a cooker when they are being supervised.) The children should already be able to identify most parts of the cooker. However, it may be worth revising this information using Copymaster 45. This sheet also encourages them to think about which parts of the cooker are used for different cooking processes. When they have completed the sheet, discuss what foods they like to eat or make and how these foods are cooked.

Task 3

Copymaster 46 focuses on the characteristics of the microwave cooker, and aims to familiarise the children with this method of cooking. However, before they start work on this sheet, they should be made aware of the differences between this piece of equipment and a cooker. Also, discuss the uses of the microwave. Can the children suggest the advantages and disadvantages of using a microwave? The advantages could include: its compact size, its suitability for use within a small kitchen or for people without a kitchen, and its easily cleaned parts. The disadvantages could include: its unsuitability for large, complex meals and the lack of a browning facility on some models.

Task 4

Ask the children to think of as many methods as they can for preserving food, e.g. salting, canning, freezing, drying, pickling, vacuum packing, refrigeration and adding preservatives, such as sugar or alcohol. Then focus on refrigeration by asking them to complete Copymaster 47, which shows the correct way to fill a fridge. Explore their knowledge of food hygiene issues, such as washing fruit and vegetables, covering food and cooking food sufficiently.

Task 5

Use Copymaster 48 to revise the basic rules of kitchen hygiene.

Answers to Copymaster 48

Before you start: Wash your hands, take off jewellery, wear an apron, tie back long hair, cover any cuts, clean the work area. *While you are working:* Never lick your fingers, wipe up spills. *After you have finished:* Wash the dishes, rinse the cloths, wipe all surfaces, sweep the floor, cover all food.

FOCUSED PRACTICAL TASKS

Materials/equipment needed: Copymasters 49, 50, 51, 52, 53 and 54; reference books about food and nutrition.

Introductory tasks

Food diary

To begin this section of work, ask the children to record everything they eat in a whole week on Copymaster 49. Then discuss what they think a healthy diet consists of and brainstorm the names of healthy and unhealthy foods. (This work could form part of a science project on health and the body.)

Food and nutrition

The children should read Copymaster 50. This provides general information about food and nutrition, and can be referred to in later activities. Copymaster 51 should then be used to reinforce this knowledge. Encourage the children to research this area further using suitable reference books.

Answers to Copymaster 51

Nutrition crossword *Answers for across:* 1. GROWTH; 2. ACTIVE; 11. SUGARS; 12. CARBOHYDRATES; 16. PLANTS; 17. JOULES; 19. DAIRY; 20. VITAMINS.

Answers for down: 2. WATER; 3. QUANTITIES; 4. POTATO; 5. ENERGY; 6. LETTERS; 7. FIBRE; 8. TASTE; 10. CALCIUM; 13. BUILDERS; 14. TABLETS; 15. BLOOD; 18. FIVE.

Classifying foods

Give the group copies of Copymaster 52 to complete. They will need to use the information already learned in this section to sort the foods into the correct categories. Then explain that some foods are more complex, as they contain more than one element.

Answers to Copymaster 52

Proteins: meat, fish, nuts, beans, cheese. *Sugars:* chocolate, jam, honey. *Fats:* yoghurt, cheese, meat, crisps, butter, nuts, milk. *Starches:* bread, pasta, potatoes, rice. *Fibres:* fruit, bread, potatoes, beans, vegetables, cereals. Water, minerals and vitamins are also important for a balanced diet.

The children should use Copymaster 53 to identify the elements present in certain foods, using colours and symbols to complete a key.

A balanced meal
(Copymasters 53 and 54 should be used to support this task.) To extend the idea of a balanced diet, the children should select some of the foods from Copymaster 53 to create a variety of lunch menus. Encourage them to incorporate as many of the elements as possible in each design. Afterwards, ask them which lunch menu they would prefer. This task leads into the Design and make assignment, which asks the children to design their own lunch.

DESIGN AND MAKE ASSIGNMENT

Aim: To design and make a healthy picnic lunch (including a slice of cheese and tomato pizza).

Materials/equipment needed: Copymasters 50, 52, 53, 54, 55, 56, 57 and 58; ingredients for the pizza recipe, containers and wrappings for a picnic lunch, picnic ingredients, kitchen scales, table knives, medium-sized bowls, sieves, forks, plastic mixing bowls, rolling-pins, baking sheets, small saucepans, sharp knives, chopping boards, graters, measuring jugs.

Introduction
Begin by organising the children into pairs. This activity could be completed individually, but working in pairs demands co-operation and communication. Also, it would be useful for each child to conduct some 'market research' into their partner's likes and dislikes. Then explain that each pair will be designing and making a mini picnic lunch which includes a slice of cheese and tomato pizza. The lunch must be healthy and well-balanced.

Designing
Copymaster 55 can be used as a starting point for the design process. This explains to the children what they are going to be doing and gives them some key questions to think about. Provide them with copies of Copymasters 56 and 57, which show the recipe for scone-based pizza. Then ask them to plan the rest of their picnic using Copymasters 50, 52, 53, and especially 54. (Remind them to use knowledge gained from the previous activities.) Emphasise that personal preferences should be taken into account, and they should discuss their likes and dislikes in pairs.

The next stage is for the children to transfer their menu plans on to Copymaster 58, using the key to show which elements are in each type of food. They should also make a shopping list on the same sheet. At this point, they decide which ingredients will be brought from home and which will be purchased by the school.

Making
First, the children should be reminded of hygiene rules, i.e. washing hands, tying up hair and putting on an apron. Then encourage them to collect all the utensils and ingredients they will need to make their lunch. Next, the pairs should read through the whole method for making the pizza, dividing out the jobs between them.

The children will need to be supervised carefully, and given guidance, while making their pizzas. Some may need help with rubbing in and use of the cooker. However, they should be encouraged to work as independently as possible.

Once the pizzas are in the oven, the children can then prepare the rest of their picnic. They will probably have brought most of the ingredients from home, and these will just require some 'assembly'. Then the picnic can be arranged in a suitable container or on a plate. They should be encouraged to arrange it in an interesting and appetising way. Hopefully, the pairs will have organised some extra trimmings, such as paper napkins, cutlery, cups and even a tablecloth between them. These should all have been included in the design.

When the pizzas are ready, they can be divided between the children, each partner having a slice and taking any surplus home.

Evaluating
Obviously the picnics are best evaluated by eating them, but the children should be given the opportunity to view all the picnics before this takes place. They should be encouraged to comment on each other's picnic layouts. A photograph of each picnic could be taken for assessment purposes.

UNIT 6: CONTROLLING ELECTRICITY

A LIGHT FOR A TEENAGE DOLL

Learning objectives

Designing skills
The children should be given the opportunity to:

- look at the development of lamps through history
- investigate different types of lamps, where they would be used and their purpose
- discover how a simple torch operates and how circuits are made
- design a lamp which is a suitable size for a teenage doll.

Making skills
The children should practise:

- using simple electrical components to make a working circuit
- using everyday materials to make a working switch
- finding faults in a simple circuit and correcting them
- selecting suitable materials from a limited range
- using electrical tools, such as wire strippers, screwdriver etc.

Knowledge and understanding
The children should learn:

- how a circuit works and how to control it with a switch
- how lamps work and how to evaluate their suitability for a specific purpose
- about safety when using electricity and the dangers of mains electricity.

Vocabulary: battery, bulb, bell-push switch, toggle switch, circuit, bulb, batten holder, clip holder, crocodile clip, wires.

INVESTIGATING TASKS

Materials/equipment needed: Copymasters 59 and 60, different types of lamps and lights, pictures of lamps from the present and past, a torch.

Task 1

Make a pictorial display to show the development of lamps through history — from the rush light or Roman oil lamp through to the candelabra and miners' safety lamps and then on to electric lights. Use Copymaster 59 to support this task.

Task 2

Observe and discuss different types of contemporary lamps. Point out how each light works. Then note their purpose and characteristics, e.g. a tall standard lamp for reading and an angle-poise lamp for working.

Task 3

Dismantle a torch and show the children how it works. Then, using Copymaster 60, explain what its circuit is made up of.

Answers to Copymaster 60

What happens when the switch is moved in the direction of the arrow? *The torch lights.* What is the spring for? *It is to keep the batteries in place and to complete the circuit.* What is the reflector for? *It is to reflect the light of the bulb and make the torch appear brighter.*

Most of the group should have done some work on basic circuits at Key Stage 1, and this would be a good opportunity to discover the extent of their knowledge and to revise basic vocabulary, e.g. battery, wire, bulb, circuit, electricity, current and switch. (This task could be linked to science work on parallel and series circuits, insulators and conductors.)

Next, look carefully at the toggle switch and show the children how it works. Remove its casing to allow them to examine the workings, and encourage them to play with the switch, watching the gap open and close as it is operated (Fig. 1).

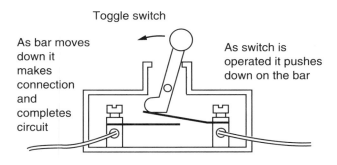

Toggle switch

As bar moves down it makes connection and completes circuit

As switch is operated it pushes down on the bar

Fig. 1

FOCUSED PRACTICAL TASKS

Materials/equipment needed: Copymasters 61 and 62, electricity sets, 4.5mm dowel, plastic tubing, MDF wheels, wire, Kodak® film canisters, split pins, paper clips, card, baking foil, drawing pins.

Introductory tasks

Circuit components

Groups of about four or five children should be issued with electricity sets. (For details of the components needed in each set see Copymaster 61.) Then, using Copymaster 61, they should identify all the different pieces of equipment. This is a useful way of checking that each set is complete, at the beginning and end of each lesson.

Independent tasks

Making a circuit

Ask the children to make a circuit using a battery in a holder, crocodile wires, a bulb and a toggle switch (Fig. 2). At this point, teach them how to check their circuit (if this process has not already been covered). First, they should check it is connected correctly and that these are good connections. Secondly, they should change each

piece of equipment in turn, starting with the battery — a dead battery is the cause of most ills! Emphasise that they should not change all the pieces of equipment at once, as this will achieve little. Copymaster 62 could be used to assist the teaching of this process.

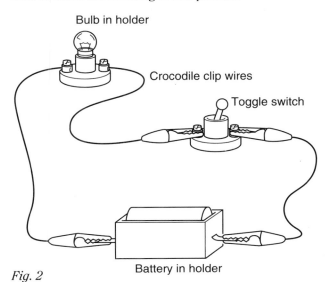

Bulb in holder

Crocodile clip wires

Toggle switch

Battery in holder

Fig. 2

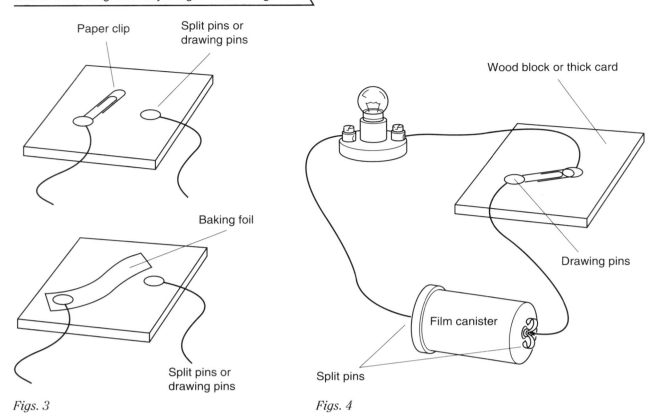

Figs. 3

Figs. 4

Once the circuit is working, the children could replace their standard battery holder with a home-made one, made from a film canister (see Traffic lights section, pages 57–60). As these are rather difficult to make, lower juniors could be given ready-made examples. They can then make a switch using two split pins and a paper clip, or a piece of card covered with baking foil. If a solid base is used, then drawing pins can take the place of the split pins (Fig. 3). Crocodile clip wires can be replaced with plain wire, the ends of which should be stripped clean of plastic. The wires may be firmly wrapped around the pins, avoiding the need for soldering (Fig. 4). NB: At each stage the circuit should be checked to make sure it is still working.

DESIGN AND MAKE ASSIGNMENT

Aim: To design and make a working light for a teenage doll to use.

Materials/equipment needed: batteries, battery holders, 1.5V bulbs, bulb holders (batten and clip), wire, wirestrippers, split pins, paper clips, drawing pins, card, art straws, wood/thick card bases, 4.5mm dowel, plastic tubing, bendy drinking straws, MDF/card wheels, thick paper (e.g. wallpaper or wrapping paper), cardboard tubes, PVA glue, pipe cleaners, baking foil, junior hacksaws, snips, drill, eyelet pliers punch, lollysticks, film canisters, reclaimed materials, sticky pads, hot glue, wire wool, sandpaper, 'teenage' dolls, jelutong lengths.

Introduction

Acquire a few 'teenage' dolls, for demonstration purposes, and ask the children to name the associated accessories available in the shops. Explain that they are going to design a working light especially for one of these dolls.

Designing

First, revise the work already completed on circuits.

Then ask the children to decide upon a purpose for which their light is to be used or the room that it will be placed in. They should keep this in mind while designing their lamp.

Next, show the class the materials that will be available to them. Demonstrate that the dowel fits snugly into the wheels to make lamp bases. The fitting can be tightened, if necessary, using a piece of plastic tubing as a washer (Fig. 5). If it is a little too tight, the dowel can be sharpened slightly in a pencil sharpener. Suggest that the dowel could be joined together using plastic tubing. If the light is to bend, as in an angle-poise lamp, the tubing can be snipped or the dowel replaced with bendy drinking straws (Fig 6). The bulb can also be made moveable by pushing a lollystick into a clip bulb holder. The first lollystick is then attached to another, or a length of jelutong, with a split pin (Fig. 7). Then show the children how to make a lampshade from a cone of paper or card by cutting away the top. Reclaimed materials, such as an egg box segment or a bottle lid, can be used for the same purpose (Figs. 8 & 9). Point out that a card circle or pipe cleaners could be used to keep

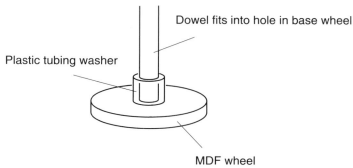

Dowel fits into hole in base wheel

Plastic tubing washer

MDF wheel

Figs. 5

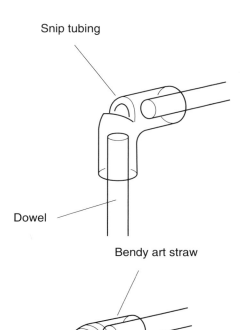

Snip tubing

Dowel

Bendy art straw

Dowel

Figs. 6

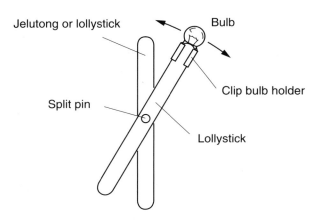

Jelutong or lollystick

Bulb

Split pin

Clip bulb holder

Lollystick

Figs. 7

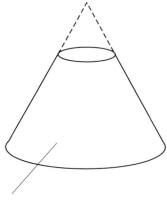

Basic cone
lampshade

Strip of paper or
card made into
concertina and
gathered with a
needle and thread

Shampoo
bottle top
decorated
with fringe

Hole made with paper punch

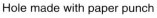
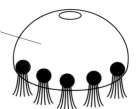

Figs. 8

Thin cardboard inner tube

Batten bulb holder

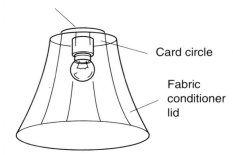

Card circle

Fabric
conditioner
lid

Figs. 9

55

the lampshade away from the bulb. On some lamps the wires are left visible, but if a child wishes to hide them, the wires and dowel will fit into a length of 6.5mm plastic tubing. The thinnest dowel (3.2mm) will even slip through a straw.

When you have discussed the uses of materials sufficiently, ask the children to draw a picture of the light that they would like to make. To produce an accurate drawing, they should measure the height of the doll they wish to use when standing, or sitting if they are going to make a desk light. They should then draw a line the same length up the side of a piece of paper. Tell them to draw their picture alongside this scale line, bearing in mind the purpose of the light and where it will be placed. The next stage is to draw in the battery, switch, bulb and wires, to remind themselves of how the circuit is constructed. The picture can then be labelled to show which materials they are going to use and the methods to be used to construct the light.

Making

The bulb holder and its base should be made first, leaving the wires trailing, to be attached to the rest of the circuit later. Remind the children not to get glue etc. over the connections, as this will act as an insulator. Also, it would be helpful to have a few 'teenage' dolls available to encourage them to measure their lights against the toys. Any modifications can therefore be made during the construction of the light, rather than waiting until the end of the project when changes are more difficult to make.

Having constructed the lamp and its base, the lampshade can be attached. This should not touch the bulb, in case the bulb gets warm, but it can be decorated with paper, fringe etc., or with baking foil to give it a more modern, metallic look or to provide a reflector for a spot-light.

The rest of the circuit should then be fitted around this and the structure of the light made.

Once the whole lamp is complete, the children should connect the wires from the light to their circuit. Having been checked, the whole model can be mounted on to a thick card or wooden base using sticky pads or hot glue. If using the latter, it is worthwhile remembering to roughen up the surfaces with wire wool or sandpaper, especially that of the battery holder, as glue tends to come unstuck if pasted directly on to smooth plastic.

Evaluating

The children were asked to design a light for a 'teenage' doll, and so the first method of evaluation is to see whether each light is a suitable size for the doll. Secondly, they were asked to make a working light, so a test can be done to see whether the models actually work or not. Thirdly, the children should guess where the doll might use each light and what it would be used for.

TRAFFIC LIGHTS

Learning objectives

Designing skills

The children should learn to design complex circuit diagrams and draw them using recognised symbols.

Making skills

The children should practise:

● using electrical components: buzzers, bulbs, switches, batteries, wires and a terminal block
● using a soldering iron, where appropriate
● combining electrical components with other materials.

Knowledge and understanding

The children should learn:

● that a battery has a positive and a negative terminal
● about more complex circuits, including parallel and series circuits
● about polarity and how to identify positive and negative terminals
● about the dangers of electricity.

Vocabulary: switch, circuit, bulb, buzzer, battery/cell, polarity, series, parallel, control, positive, negative, terminal.

INVESTIGATING TASKS

Materials/equipment needed: Copymasters 62, 63, 64 and 65; electricity sets (for details see Copymaster 61), extra bulbs and bulb holders, crocodile wires, batteries, buzzers, reed switches, magnets, card, paper clips, split pins.

To complete the following tasks, the children will need to have some knowledge of circuits and be able to make up a simple circuit that includes a bulb, buzzer etc. Also, before embarking upon these tasks, use Copymaster 63 to revise the names of electrical components. (The components are as Copymaster 61 except for number 7 which is a reed switch.)

Task 1
Ask the children to make up a circuit using a single battery in a battery holder, a bulb and a toggle switch. They can use the Circuit trouble shooter chart on Copymaster 62 if there are any problems with the circuit, or if they wish to adapt it. They should then note how brightly the bulb is lit.

Task 2
Ask the children to replace the toggle switch with a reed switch. Demonstrate how the reed switch operates when a magnet is placed nearby. Copymaster 65 can be then used to illustrate the differences between the types of switch.

Answers to Copymaster 65
Switching on
Toggle switch The toggle level pushes down on the bar causing it to touch the connection on the left, thereby completing the circuit. The circuit remains closed until the switch is moved back to its off position.
Bell-push switch As the switch is pressed it forces the two metal bars to touch and completes the circuit. When the switch is released the bars spring back to their off position.
Reed switch As the magnet is brought closer to the switch it attracts the steel rods. These touch and complete the circuit. When the magnet is withdrawn the rods return to their original off position

Task 3
The children should then add another bulb to the circuit, as shown in Fig. 1. Tell them that this is called a series circuit. Is the first bulb as bright, brighter or dimmer than it was in Task 1?

Task 4
Ask the children to remove the second bulb and place it in parallel with the first one (Fig. 2). Is the first bulb the same, brighter or dimmer than Task 1?

Task 5
The children should then place all three bulbs in series (Fig. 3) and test them.

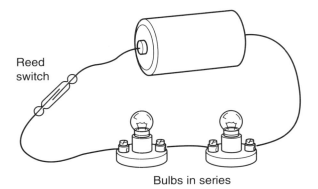

Reed switch

Bulbs in series

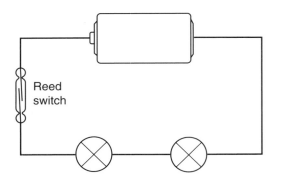

Reed switch

Fig. 1

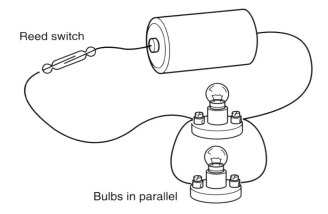

Reed switch

Bulbs in parallel

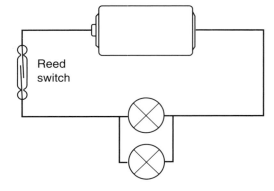

Reed switch

Fig. 2

58

Task 6
Finally, the children should place all three bulbs in parallel (Fig. 4) and test them.

Task 7
Tell the children to make up a double circuit, as shown in Fig. 5. The circuit needs to include a battery and switch, which should be made of a paper clip attached to a piece of card with a split pin. The switch should be connected to two other split pins, thereby linking the battery to two circuits — one with a bulb and the other with a buzzer.

Task 8
The children should complete the comprehension task about Michael Faraday on Copymaster 64.

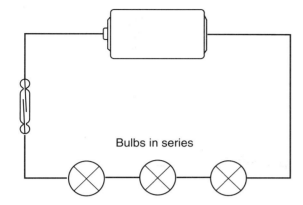

Bulbs in series

Fig. 3

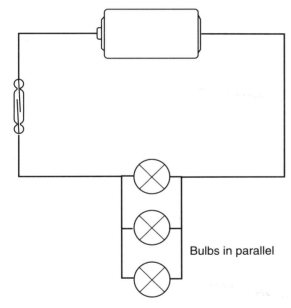

Bulbs in parallel

Fig. 3

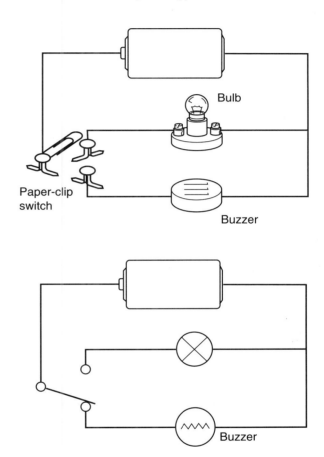

Fig. 5

FOCUSED PRACTICAL TASKS

Materials needed: Copymaster 66, LEDs (light emitting diodes) in red, yellow and green; batteries, film canisters, battery holders, split pins, drawing pins, paper clips, batten bulb holders, wires, wire strippers, soldering iron, correx or wood bases, sticky pads, tape.

Independent tasks

Designing a 'traffic lights' circuit
To complete this activity, the children will need to know how to make a home-made battery holder from a film canister and a switch, using split pins or drawing pins and paper clips. First, explain that they are going to make a circuit for a traffic light system. Then provide them with paper on which to draw a diagram of a circuit which has three lights (red, amber and green) that operate independently from one battery. Next, tell them that the battery holder is to be made from a film canister (Fig. 6). The switch should be made from paper clips, and should allow a number of circuits to be connected up, one after the other. This should be fixed on to the base, even if the other elements of the circuit are loose (Fig 7).

Use grey-lidded film canisters

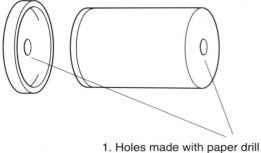

2. Stick split pin onto pencil with Blu-tak®, and push through hole

3. Push pin through lid

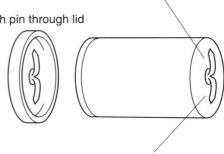

1. Holes made with paper drill

4. Fold ends out

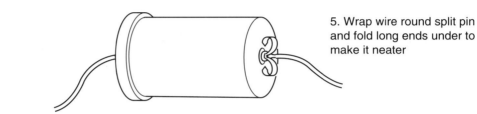

5. Wrap wire round split pin and fold long ends under to make it neater

6. Wrap wire round pin on lid

7. Put battery inside and push lid on firmly

Fig. 6

Twist strands together

Twist wires around paper clip

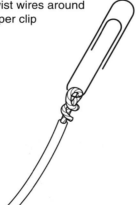

Home-made 3-way switch

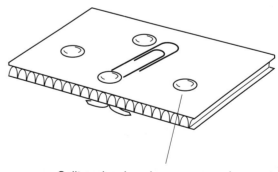

Split or drawing pins near enough for paper clip to touch

Fig. 7

The children should draw their circuit diagrams and check them carefully. (Copymaster 66 can be used to support this task.) Individuals who find this task difficult to complete should be given help in the form of a pre-drawn circuit diagram. (Fig. 8)

Making 'traffic lights'
Following the design stage, the children can use electricity kits to make up their circuits. If resources are limited, this activity can be done in groups, but ideally each child should have the opportunity to try out his/her own design. Although using LEDs makes colour identification easier, the circuit can be made using ordinary 1.5V bulbs — as long as they are clearly labelled with the colours red, amber and green.

Before the children begin to make their circuits, it is important that they are made aware of polarity. This means that a device such as a buzzer or LED will only work in one direction, and must therefore be connected up correctly. Usually, this means that the red wire should be connected to the positive (+) side of the battery and the black wire to the negative (−) side of the battery.

The children should then proceed to make their circuits. (At this stage, the circuits do not need to be made permanent. Each circuit, or at least the components, will need to be used in the Design and make assignment.) They will need to be taught how to strip wires, using a wire stripper, and should be encouraged to use circuit connectors, rather than twisting wires together. The LEDs may need to be soldered. If the children have not yet had experience of using a soldering iron, this would be a good opportunity to cover this skill, but for speed and safety it may be more convenient to have the soldering done prior to the project (see Tools section, p. 114).

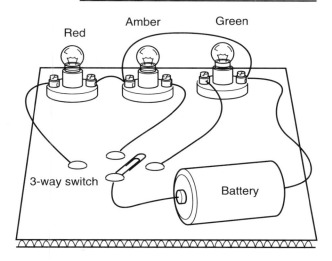

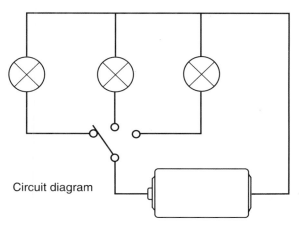

Circuit diagram

Fig. 8

DESIGN AND MAKE ASSIGNMENT

Aim: To design and make working traffic lights that include a 'cross' signal for a blind person.

Materials/equipment needed: Copymaster 66, batteries, battery holders, LEDs/bulbs, batten bulbs, bulb holders, wires, wire strippers, soldering iron, correx or wood bases, split pins, drawing pins, paper clips, buzzers, screwdrivers, cardboard boxes, cardboard inner tubes, sticky pads, tape, ramin, glue-guns, hacksaws, bench hooks.

Introduction
As the children have already made the circuit for their traffic lights, little introduction to this project is really needed. However, the design brief should be studied

carefully, as it states that the traffic lights should include a cross signal for a blind person. The children may need to be reminded that this will have to be an audible signal, and that it must operate when the traffic lights are red. More able individuals may be able to work this out for themselves.

Designing
The children should use the work that they have already done in the Focused practical tasks section as the basis for this assignment. They will need to incorporate a buzzer into their original circuit design. This should operate when the red light is lit, i.e. when the cars are stopped. (Copymaster 66 can be used to support this task.) The resulting circuit will be more or less as shown

in Fig. 9. The children should be reminded that the buzzer has polarity, and therefore only works in one direction. It should also be noted that it is best connected in parallel to the red bulb, rather than in series, as a drop in voltage may prevent the bulb or buzzer from operating (Fig. 10).

Having designed the circuit, the children must then design the traffic lights into which the bulbs are to be positioned. They should already be aware of the size of the bulbs, buzzer and battery, and will therefore be able to estimate the size of the support needed. This must be free-standing. Their design should be in the form of an annotated diagram, showing the positioning of the bulbs.

Next, the children should write an action plan. This should consist of a numbered list of tasks which they can follow when making up their circuit and traffic-light support.

Making

Before allowing the children to begin this activity, revise safety rules. They should then work as independently as possible to complete the project. (If the making process varies from the action plan, they should record these deviations on the plan.) Encourage them to use the components from their previous circuit with the addition of a buzzer. This time, the components will need to be fixed more permanently using circuit connectors and solder. Also, emphasise that their finished product should be of a good quality. Remind the children to test their circuit a few times during the making process. However, repeated testing will run the battery down, not to mention the teacher!

Evaluating

The children should demonstrate their models to the rest of the class. They can then be discussed in terms of appearance and operation. Finally, the projects should be displayed with a portfolio of design work.

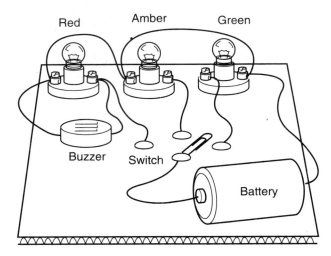

Fig. 9

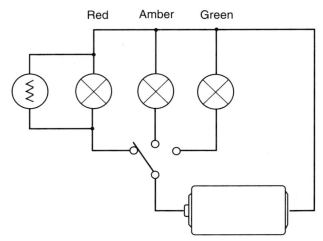

Fig. 10

UNIT 7: LEVERS

LOLLIPOP-STICK PUPPETS

Learning objectives

Designing skills
The children should be given the opportunity to:

- use paper and card to model lever mechanisms
- evaluate ideas in order to choose the most appropriate one for a specific purpose and user.

Making skills
The children should practise:

- cutting and shaping paper and card using scissors and snips
- using a punch and hole punch to make holes
- using a needle and thread, tape, glue and split pins to join materials.

Knowledge and understanding
The children should learn:

- about products that use levers
- that a lever is a rigid beam that rotates about a pivot or fulcrum
- that one end of the lever travels further than the other end
- that levers are used to increase force
- that levers are used for pushing and pulling.

Vocabulary: lever, pivot, beam, push/pull, prototype.

INVESTIGATING TASKS

Materials/equipment needed: Copymaster 67, a collection of levers, pictures of levers, books and videos about levers, card, split pins, eyelet pliers, punches, lollysticks, coloured pencils.

Task 1

Define a lever, i.e. a rigid beam that rotates around a pivot or fulcrum. Discuss this definition and, if possible, watch videos about levers or show the children pictures of different types. Then explain that levers are often used to increase the force we wish to use, e.g. opening a tin of paint with a screwdriver or lifting a rock with a crowbar (Fig. 1). Identify inventions that have used levers, e.g. the typewriter, the sewing machine and the door handle.

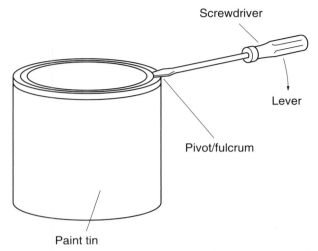

Fig. 1

Answers to Copymaster 67

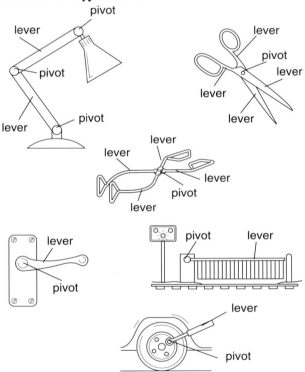

Fig. 2

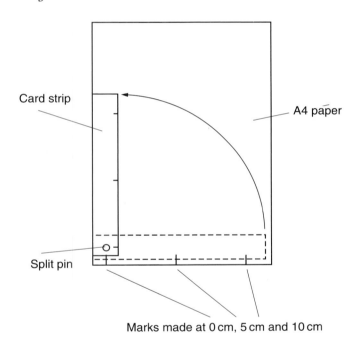

Make a collection of objects that contain levers found around the school, and ask children to bring in some from home, e.g. scissors, jar openers, garlic presses, tweezers, toy dumper trucks, angle-poise lamps, hole punches, staplers, etc. Identify the lever and the pivot in each one. Then use Copymaster 67 to reinforce this work. Figure 2 shows the answer to Copymaster 67.

Task 2

Demonstrate that one end of a lever travels a long way, but the end close to the pivot only moves a short distance (Fig. 3). Then provide each child with a piece of A4 paper, a strip of card and a split pin. Ask them to

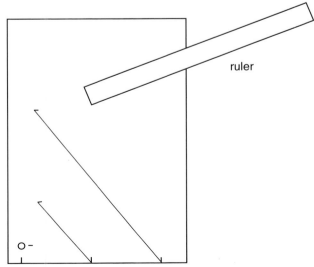

Fig. 3

65

attach the end of the card strip to corner of the paper with the split pin, and, with a ruler, mark off 0cm, 5cm and 10cm along one edge of the card and paper. They should then rotate the card strip through 90° and mark the paper at 0cm, 5cm and 10 cm. Next, ask them to measure the distances between the pairs of marks.

When the marks are joined up it can be seen that the end further from the pivot moves farther than the other end. This experiment proves that the further you are from the pivot, the greater the distance moved.

Task 3
Give each child a strip of card 20cm × 3cm and a square of card 10cm × 10cm. Ask them to measure 15cm along

the middle of the strip and mark this place with a dot. They must then make a small hole there with the point of a pencil. Tell them to make another small hole in the top left quadrant of the square. The correct area could be located by folding the card into four (if it is flexible enough), or by drawing a diagram on the blackboard. The strip of card must then be attached behind/to the back of it using a split pin. A figure could be drawn and stuck to the end of the strip. Moving the strip down should allow the figure to pop up from behind the square (Fig. 4).

Afterwards, the children could compare the levers made for Tasks 2 and 3.

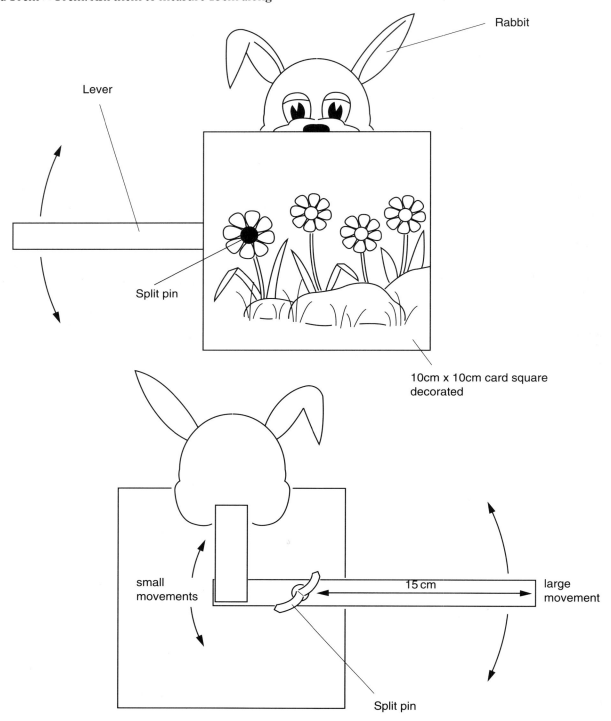

Rabbit

Lever

Split pin

10cm x 10cm card square decorated

small movements

15 cm

large movement

Split pin

Fig. 4

66

FOCUSED PRACTICAL TASKS

Materials/equipment needed: lollysticks, card circles/paper plates, tape, PVA glue, wool/string, crayons, felt pens, eyelet pliers punch.

Fig. 5

In preparation for the following tasks, punch a hole in the end of each lollystick (three per child) using eyelet pliers punch and draw and cut out card circles with a diameter of 10cm.

Introductory tasks

Making lollystick mechanisms
Demonstrate how lollysticks can be joined together to form X, Y and Z shapes (Fig. 6). Then, for each, show what type of movement has been created.

Independent tasks

Making a lollipop-stick puppet
Ask the children to make a Y-shaped mechanism, as

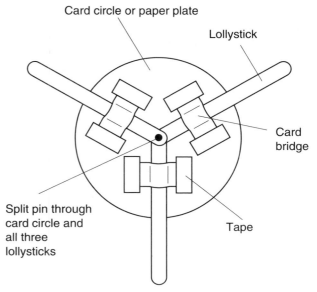

Fig. 7

shown previously. This should be positioned on the back of a circle of card and secured with 'bridges' of taped-down card and a split pin (Fig. 7). The 'bridges' are intended to hold the lollysticks in place while allowing the movement to work. The card circle can now be decorated to show a human or animal face. (With older pupils this could be done before the lollysticks are secured, but younger pupils may have difficulties aligning the Y shape correctly.) Next the ears and food can be made and attached to the lollysticks with glue, making sure that the food reaches the mouth when the mechanism is operated (see Figs. 5 and 8).

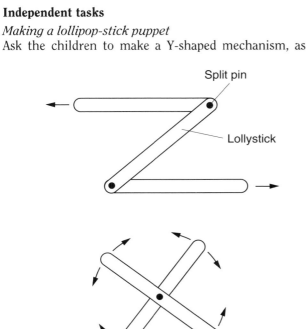

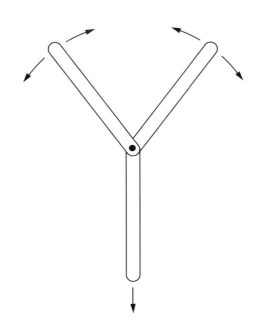

Fig. 6

Design ideas

Fig. 8

DESIGN AND MAKE ASSIGNMENT

Aim: To design and make a prototype for a moving toy that is linked to a character from a children's book.

Materials/equipment needed: Copymasters 68 and 69, a collection of items whose design has been inspired by books, films, TV etc.; card, lollysticks, string/thick thread, beads, needles, split pins, scissors, PVA glue, clear tape.

Introduction

Read Copymaster 68 aloud. It states that a publishing company intends to produce a new series of children's books, and they wish to create a set of toys to be merchandised alongside these. Explain that they have decided to seek expert advice, i.e. from children. Then show them some items whose design has been inspired by forms of media, e.g. books, films etc. Discuss the reasons for producing these objects — i.e. to promote the original product and make money and their attraction, particularly for children! Also talk about the meaning of the word 'prototype', and explain they do not have to make a saleable article, but more a working model to illustrate their ideas to the manufacturer.

Designing

Encourage the children to look through books at home and/or at school to identify suitable characters on which to base their design. (At this point it may be desirable to limit the task by specifying an age range at which the product is aimed, such as infant or lower junior.) Then ask them to draw and colour small pictures of the possible characters — preferably standing frontal views. They must then choose one to develop further, and a larger, more detailed drawing of this should be made. This picture can be annotated to show colours, patterns, etc.

Making

Copymaster 69 can be used to support this task. Show the children a model of the Y-shaped lever puppet design (made in Focused practical tasks) and revise the method of construction. Then provide them with four lollysticks each, and demonstrate how to make holes in these, using the eyelet pliers punch. For each, one hole must be at the end and another made about 2cm in from this. (This task can be performed individually, or in small groups with the help of an adult.) Then a length of thread about 60cm long should be cut and threaded through the end hole of one lollystick using a needle (leaving one long end) and secured with a knot (Fig. 9). This process should then be repeated for all four lollysticks.

The next stage is to cut two pieces of card 10cm x 10cm and punch holes in the corners of each using a standard hole punch. If both pieces of card are punched together, the holes will match up. Then the lollysticks should be attached to the card with the split pins to make a

'sandwich' of card, lollystick, card, making sure that each split pin goes through the second, inner hole of each stick. Afterwards the pins can be opened out, taking care not to press them down too tightly or the lollysticks will not operate smoothly (Fig. 10).

Once all the lollysticks have been attached to the card, the threads can be brought together on one side. These can be tied together after it has been checked that the arms and legs are all pointing downwards. A bead should then be threaded on to the four strings and tied in a large knot (Fig. 11).

The children can then proceed to decorate their puppets. First, they need to draw and cut out a 10cm x 10cm square on card as a basis for the character. From here, the decoration of the square largely depends on each individual's designs. For example, the square may be extended to add a skirt, cape, coat and so on. It must be remembered that trousers, sleeves, etc. must be made separately, so that they can be attached to the lollysticks. Then, once the body has been drawn it can be coloured, cut out and glued in position on the model with PVA glue or similar. A staple under each arm may be used in an emergency! Next, a head with a 4cm-long neck should be drawn and cut out. This should be decorated and attached to the back of body with tape (Fig. 13). The puppet can then be further decorated with sequins, beads, feathers etc.

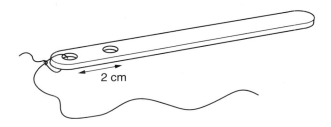

Fig. 9

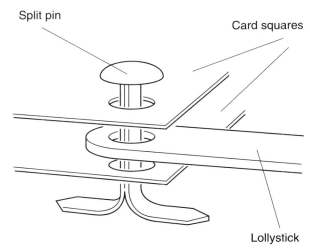

Fig. 10

69

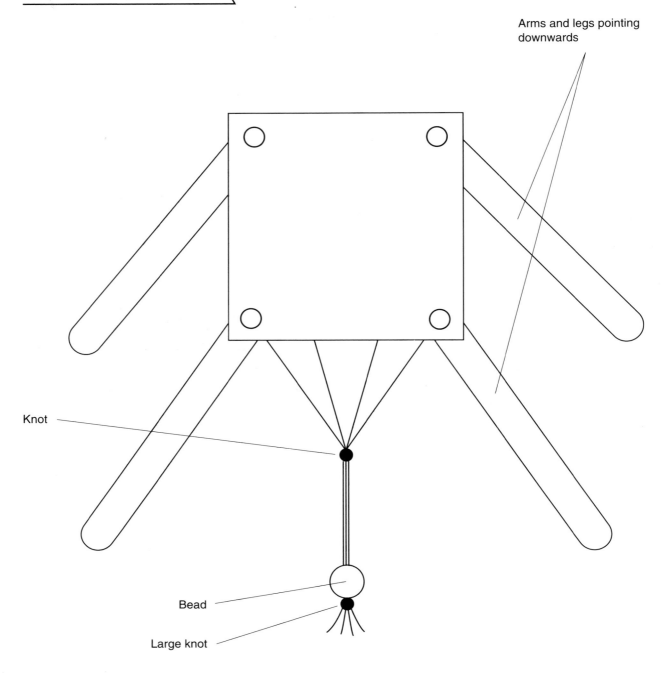

Arms and legs pointing downwards

Knot

Bead

Large knot

Fig. 11

Evaluating

The children should be encouraged to evaluate each other's work, giving constructive criticism. Then puppets can be displayed on a wall, together with the designs and even the books from which they originated.

'TAP TURNERS'

Learning objectives

Designing skills
The children should be given the opportunity to:

- use their previous knowledge of levers and products incorporating levers
- draw scale drawings in order to achieve an accurate design
- use squared paper in order to produce accurate drawings
- produce annotated or exploded diagrams to show methods of construction.

Making skills
The children should practise:

- tracing and making patterns
- using snips or art knives and a safety ruler
- choosing appropriate materials and methods of joining
- cutting and shaping wood using a junior hacksaw, and a benchhook
- cut wire using wire cutters or pliers
- thorough testing of device.

Knowledge and understanding
The children should learn:

- to evaluate products that use levers
- that the greater the distance from the pivot/fulcrum, the smaller the force needed
- that there are three different types of lever
- that careful measurement and testing will produce a more useful device.

Vocabulary: lever, pivot, effort, load, 'finish', modify.

INVESTIGATING TASKS

Materials needed: Copymasters 70 and 71, a heavy object, a seesaw balance, balance weights, 100g weights, a spring balance, string, rulers, pencils, a collection of objects that use different types of lever.

Task 1

Explain that levers are mechanisms used to increase effort. The greater the distance between the pivot (fulcrum) and the force being applied, the greater the effect, and the longer the lever, the less effort required. Then, using a pencil as a pivot and a ruler as the lever, demonstrate that it is easier to lift a heavy object — e.g. a box or paint tin — by pushing down on the end of the lever rather than the middle (Fig. 1). Next, ask a child to close the door using one finger near to the hinges. (Beware of trapping fingers in the door!) Repeat the experiment, asking them to push in the middle of the door and then at the side furthest from the hinges. Again, this should demonstrate that the longer the lever, the easier the task (Fig. 2).

Task 2

Set up the seesaw balance with a balance weight suspended halfway along one side, i.e. point 5 on side A. Balance this with a weight suspended in a similar position on side B. This illustrates that when the load and effort are at an equal distance from the fulcrum they balance (Fig. 3). Then add another balance weight to side A at point 5, thus doubling the load. Ask the children to suggest ways of making the seesaw balance again. No doubt they will suggest adding another weight at point 5 on side B. Show them that this is correct. Ask them to suggest an alternative method that uses only the one weight. They will usually suggest moving the weight on side B outwards. Show them that this is correct. If a weight is placed at point 10 on side B, it will balance the two weights at point 5 (Fig. 4). This is due to the distance from the pivot to point 10 being twice the distance from the pivot to point 5. In conclusion, for the seesaw to balance, the force multiplied by the distance must be equal on both sides, i.e. 2 weights on point 5 balances 1 weight on point 10, $2 \times 5 = 1 \times 10$. Use Copymaster 70 to reinforce this work.

Task 3

There are three types of lever. Use the following experiments to introduce them. Then show the children examples of each type. For the experiments, you could use a balance which has a horizontal bar that can be attached to the upright in various positions, but as few schools have access to this apparatus, the experiments have been illustrated using a standard seesaw balance.

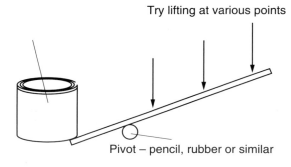

Fig. 1

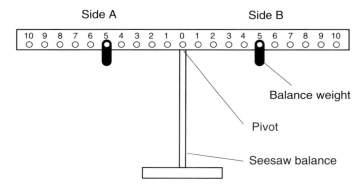

Fig. 3

Fig. 2

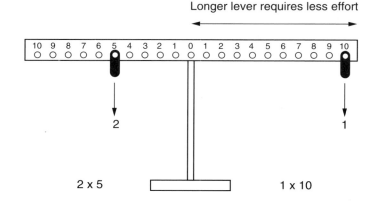

Fig. 4

72

First-class lever
The pivot is between the load (weight) and the effort (Fig. 5).

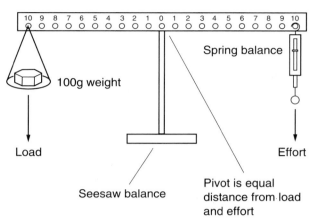

Fig. 5

The balance should be set up so that load — in this case a 100g weight — is suspended from the end of the seesaw balance, the spring balance is attached to the other end, and the pivot is in the middle. The load and the effort are at equal distances from the pivot, so the spring balance should show the load's normal weight. Moving the load nearer to the pivot creates an advantage, i.e. the lever is longer and so the effort needed will decrease. Examples of first-class levers are scissors, pliers, tongs, shears and crowbars.

Second-class lever
The load is between the effort and the pivot (Fig. 6).
The balance should be set up so that the 100g weight is attached to a point halfway along the balance and the force is applied at the end of the same side. Although the

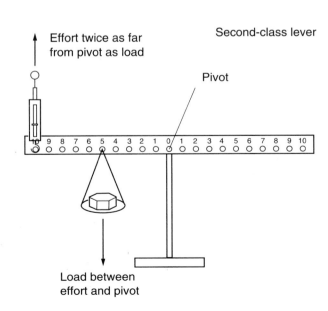

Fig. 6

load and effort are equal distances apart, the effort is twice as far from the pivot. This creates a long lever, and the spring balance shows a reduced effort compared to the previous experiment. Moving the weight closer to the pivot will reduce the effort and produce a greater advantage.

Examples of second-class levers are nutcrackers, garlic presses, wheelbarrows and hole punches.

Third-class lever
The effort is between the pivot and the load (Fig. 7).

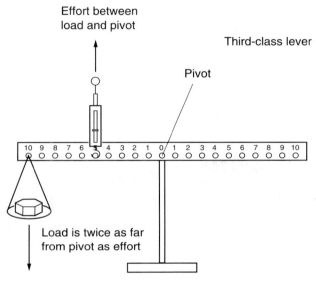

Fig. 7

The balance should be set up so that the load is suspended at the end of the balance and the spring balance is halfway along on the same side. The effort and the load are the same distance apart, but the load is twice as far from the pivot as the effort. Therefore, the spring balance shows an increased effort, as the lever is very short. Although it is harder to work this system than the other two, this can be an advantage when dealing with delicate loads where control is needed.

Examples of third-class levers are sugar tongs, tweezers and the lower arm (Fig. 8).

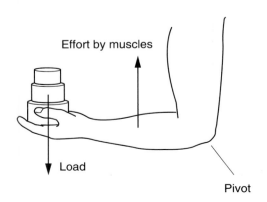

Fig. 8

Copymaster 71 can be used to revise the work covered in this section. Figure 9 shows the correctly completed Copymaster sheet

Answers to Copymaster 71

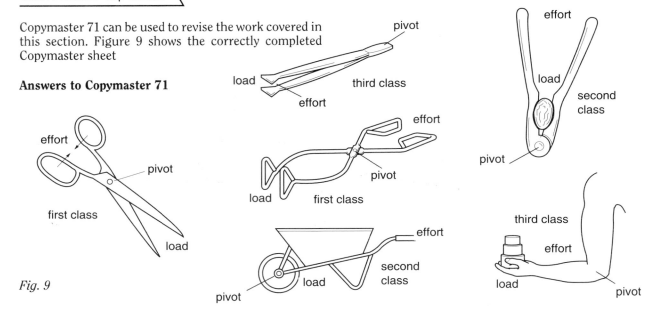

Fig. 9

FOCUSED PRACTICAL TASKS

Materials/equipment needed: Copymaster 72, tracing paper, strong card/corrugated plastic, snips/art knives, safety rulers, cutting mats, split pins, dowel, junior hacksaws, benchhooks, PVA glue, clear tape, drawing pins, rubber pads/Blutak®/Velcro®, tracing paper.

Introductory tasks
First, hold a general discussion about the practical problems that disabled and aged people encounter. Then tell the children that they are going to make a tool to help someone in a wheelchair, or someone who cannot bend very well, to pick up an object from the floor.

Making the 'helping hand'
Start by asking the children to trace the pattern shown on Copymaster 72 on to corrugated plastic or thick card. The two pieces must then be cut out, either using snips or an art knife in conjunction with a safety ruler and cutting mat. (However, before they begin cutting, remind them how to use these tools safely.) They should be joined at the marked points using a split pin or something similar. A sharp pencil will make a

sufficiently large hole for a split pin to fit through, but to ensure free movement, a paper drill or hole punch should be used (Fig. 10).

Next, ask the children to make some handles for the tool out of card dowel. However, they must first decide how long the handles need to be. The children should work in pairs to discover this, with one child measuring how much needs to be added to the length of the tool for their partner to work it when they are in a sitting position. Once made, the handles can be attached using glue or tape. Finally, encourage the children to test their finished device by trying to pick up items of varying size.

Extension activity
To extend the activity, ask the children to modify the tool in order to make it better at picking things up. Rubber pads, Blu-tack® or Velcro® could be added to the ends to increase its ability to grasp smaller objects, or a magnet could be attached to pick up small metal items (Fig. 11). Some individuals might like to make a collapsible tool, using drawing pins to attach the handles so that they can fold back.

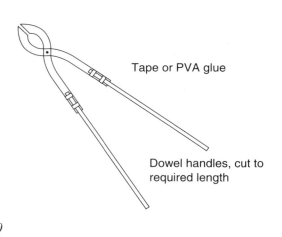

Tape or PVA glue

Dowel handles, cut to required length

Fig. 10

Card square

Small piece of card attaches card square to tool

Velcro® stuck to face of card square

Fig. 11

DESIGN AND MAKE ASSIGNMENT

Aim: To design and make a device to help an elderly/arthritic person turn on the tap.

Materials/equipment needed: Copymaster 73, scraps of wood, ramin/jelutong, strong card, junior hacksaws, bench hooks, fabric scraps (preferably strong fabrics, e.g. leather, corduroy, denim), snips, wire, wire cutters, rubber bands, drawing pins, split pins, PVA glue, small nails, hammers, glue guns, a collection of different styles of tap fitting, squared paper.

Introduction

If possible, invite in an elderly, disabled or arthritic friend to come into school in order to explain the problems they encounter with everyday jobs. Ask them if they find it difficult to turn on a tap? Then explain that the children are going to help them by designing a device to make turning on taps easier. (Although several commercially made devices are available it is advisable to avoid showing the group these until the end of the project.)

The design of the tool should be left as much as possible to the children. However, Copymaster 73 could be used to give them some guidance.

Designing

Ask the children to look at the different types of tap heads around the school and at home and, if possible, make a class collection of the different styles of tap fitting. Select one tap in the school to use as a prop. This should ideally be a tap that is near to the working area, e.g. in a wet area, cooking area, staffroom or, if all else fails, a nearby toilet. The pairs or groups of individuals should measure the tap carefully and draw a diagram of it to work from. If this activity would cause too much disruption or overcrowding, make one drawing in advance and photocopy this for the class to use for reference.

The next stage is for the children to draw a few designs each, and then as a group choose the best one to develop. Remind them that this should not necessarily be the best drawing but rather the most practical idea. Encourage the use of squared or graph paper to facilitate accurate drawing. Also, their designs should show the materials to be used, and should be annotated to show how each device is to be put together. Figs 12 and 13 suggest two examples for possible designs.

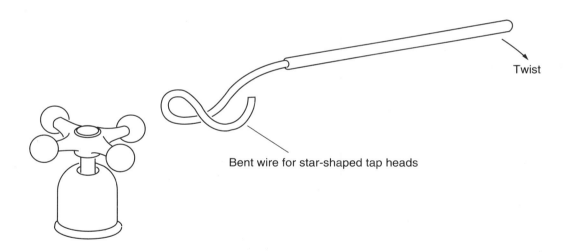

Twist

Bent wire for star-shaped tap heads

Fig. 12

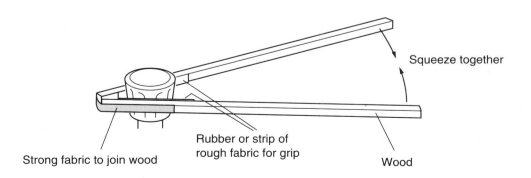

Squeeze together

Rubber or strip of rough fabric for grip

Strong fabric to join wood

Wood

Fig. 13

Making

As far as possible, this process should be directed by the children. However, it may be necessary to revise basic safety rules to follow when cutting, gluing, etc. Also remind them that their finished product should be of a good quality. They should be encouraged to test their device a few times during the making process to ensure that their design is achievable. If problems are encountered, the design can be modified, but the children are expected to record these changes as they proceed.

Evaluating

The device must be thoroughly tested at the end of the project. If a visitor was involved in the setting of the task, it would be beneficial to invite him or her to evaluate the results. This adds purpose to the whole project and means that the evaluation is more objective. Otherwise, the devices should be tested for ease of use — i.e. one handed — and also for effectiveness to see whether the device will operate the tap or not! Consideration should be given to how the device looks and feels. Finally, the children could complete a project report, noting any changes from their original design, the effectiveness of their device and any modifications that would need to be made before it could be manufactured. They could also be asked to give a short presentation, as if to a potential manufacturer of the product.

UNIT 8: WHEELS AND AXLES

A 2D CHASSIS

Learning objectives

Designing skills
The children should be given the opportunity to:

- study the mechanisms of various moving toys
- discuss who a vehicle is made for and how they would use it
- create a design from a basic shape, bearing in mind both its purpose and user
- plan a recipe for making their model.

Making skills
The children should practise:

- following a step-by-step approach to making
- joining, measuring and cutting wood accurately
- using a junior hacksaw and benchhook correctly
- joining wood, using card triangles, to make a 2D frame
- making and aligning axle holders and cutting dowel to fit
- cutting, scoring and constructing a net accurately
- cutting out and sticking shapes, neatly, for decoration
- testing and evaluating a final product.

Knowledge and understanding
The children should learn:

- how wheels are used to move a vehicle
- that the wheels must be fixed when the axle is loose, but wheels can be loose when the axle is fixed.
- how bearings are used to attach the axle
- about nets
- about car design and understand that vehicles have different characteristics.

Vocabulary: hacksaw, benchhook, 2D frame, axle, bearing, hubcap, wheel, net, evaluate, score, fold/reverse fold.

INVESTIGATING TASKS

Materials/equipment needed: Copymaster 74, a collection of moving toys, pictures of cars from books, films and newspapers.

Task 1
Provide the children with copies of Copymaster 74. Ask them to match the pictures to the correct pieces of information. Alternatively, the sheet can be made into a memory game by sticking it on to card and cutting out the squares. To play the game, the children must place the cards face down on the table. Then they must take it in turns to select two cards and turn them face up. If the cards are a matching pair, they can be removed from the table and another turn taken. If they are not matching, the cards must be placed face down again and the next player takes a turn. The game continues until all of the cards are paired up.

Task 2
Ask the children to bring in different types of moving toys from home. Help individuals to describe how one of their toys works to the rest of the class. Then encourage the group to examine their mechanisms. Each child should draw one of the toys and write a few sentences about its mechanism.

Task 3
Using pictures of vehicles from films, books, newspapers etc., ask the children to describe each car and the type of person who would drive it. They should concentrate on the character of the person, and on the type of car they might drive, e.g. fast, colourful, practical, slow, unusual. They could then design a car for a person they know.

FOCUSED PRACTICAL TASKS

Materials/equipment needed: Copymasters 29, 30 and 75; ramin/jelutong, junior hacksaws, PVA glue, card triangles, bench hooks, 4.5mm dowel, MDF wheels, plastic tubing, Connect-O-Mec® tubing, clothes pegs, biro tubes, rubber bands, rubber plumbing O-rings/pipe insulation foam, set squares, glue guns, centimetre-squared paper.

Introductory tasks

Making a 2D chassis
(In preparation for these tasks, make copies of Copymasters 29 and 30 on to card.) In order for the chassis to be used with the net for a car body on Copymaster 78, the chassis will need to be 13 cm × 6 cm. Each child will need approximately half a metre of jelutong or ramin and some card triangles. Ask them to measure and cut two lengths of ramin or jelutong 15 cm in length. (If they are unfamiliar with the technique for using benchhooks and junior hacksaws this is an ideal opportunity to introduce it – see Techniques, tools and storage, page 111.) They should then cut two lengths of ramin 5 cm long. Having cut all four lengths of wood, the children must arrange them as shown in Fig. 1. To achieve accurate right angles, set squares or more simply mats made of laminated centimetre-squared paper should be used. (Copymaster 30 is centimetre-squared).

The next stage is for the wood to be joined together using card triangles. The triangles must be stuck carefully across the corners, on both sides of the frame, using a layer of PVA glue. A glue gun could be used, but this is not usually necessary.

Independent tasks

Making axle holders and bearings
Next, the children should attach axles and bearings to their chassis. There are various ways of making axle

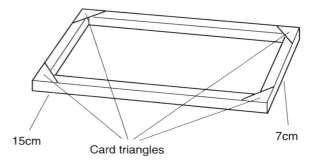
15cm   Card triangles   7cm

Fig. 1

holders or bearings — described on Copymaster 75: either the wheel is attached to the axle, and the whole thing turns freely, or the axle is static and just the wheels revolve. If the wheels and axle are both free, the vehicle won't go far! If the vehicle is to be used for experiments, e.g. trying out various wheels, then twisting rubber bands around the axles or holding the axle tight with clothes pegs is ideal. This allows the axles, with wheels attached, to be easily interchanged. Otherwise, it is better to use plastic-pen casings or similar. If the children do use plastic components, they must be reminded to roughen up the surfaces with sandpaper before gluing, to increase adhesion.

Making wheels
Wheels for the vehicle can be made using a variety of materials from jam-jar lids to commercially produced wooden wheels. The turned birch-wood wheels are rather expensive, and home-made wheels tend to be a little too flexible, therefore, MDF wheels are usually a good compromise. Tyres can be made from rubber plumbing O-rings, or from lengths of pipe insulation foam. (When linking wheels together to make a caterpillar track, corrugated card is an ideal material to use.)

If it is difficult to fit the axle into the hole in the wheel, sharpen the end of the axle with a pencil sharpener. Also, to prevent the wheels coming off the axles, either stick a bead on the end or cut a short length of tubing to slip over them. If the wheels have to be removed frequently, a rubber band twisted around the end of the axle will be sufficient.

DESIGN AND MAKE ASSIGNMENT

Aim: To design and make a moving vehicle for a book, TV or film character.

Materials/equipment needed: Copymasters 76, 77, 78, 79 and 105; the chassis from Focused practical tasks, card nets, thin card, gluesticks, PVA glue, scissors, rulers, safety rulers, clear plastic, coloured paper, plastic tubing, baking foil, glue guns, beads, fabric scraps, felt-tip pens, paints, self adhesive stickers.

Introduction
Display some toy vehicles, e.g. a collection of matchbox cars or similar. Discuss the differences between cars, and the characteristics of different vehicles. Also, if possible, make a collection of pictures of cars belonging to famous people or characters from films, TV or books to show the children, e.g. Chitty Chitty Bang Bang, Herbie, Lady Penelope's car from Thunderbirds and the Batmobile. Then explain that they are going to make a moving vehicle for a book, TV or film character.

Designing
The children should choose a book, film or TV character, preferably one that does not already have a vehicle associated with it, to design a vehicle for. They should then draw a picture of the character — with the aid of books, pictures etc, and also a picture of the vehicle that they would be driving on the outline on Copymaster 76. The children already have a basic chassis, made in the Focused practical tasks, and so should now think about how their vehicle will be decorated.

Next, encourage the children to plan the making process using a recipe approach. Copymaster 77 can be used to teach this skill.

Answers to Copymaster 77
Making my car
Use a ruler to measure the wood. Mark the wood with a pencil. Cut two shorter lengths of wood using a junior hacksaw. Position the pieces in a rectangle shape. Cut some card triangles for the corners. Stick the first side together using card corners. Turn the frame over and stick corners on the second side.

They should then write an 'ingredients list', of the materials that they will need, and a tools list. Copymaster 105 can be used to support this task. These plans should be discussed as a group to eliminate any unrealistic ones.

Making
Using Copymaster 78 photocopied onto thin card, the children should carefully colour and cut out the net for the car body. (Older, more experienced children could modify the net or even draw their own. This is made easier by photocopying centimetre squares from Copymaster 30 onto thin card.) Once the card net has been cut out, the dotted lines should be scored using a pair of scissors and a safety ruler. The dashed line should then be scored on the reverse. Having folded along the scored lines, the children can fold the body tabs inwards and stick them with a gluestick.

Before attaching the body, the children must check that it fits neatly onto the chassis and does not interfere with the movement of the wheels. If necessary, two semi-circles could be cut out on each side of the body to fit around the axles (Fig 2). The lower edges of the body can then be folded and stuck to the wooden base with PVA glue.

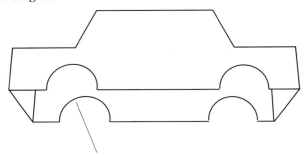

Cut out semi-circles to fit around axles

Fig. 2

The next step is to decorate the body, using paper or clear plastic for windows, plastic tubing covered in tin foil for bumpers, beads for headlamps etc. The children should be encouraged to personalise the cars as much as possible, bearing in mind the character that they are designing the car for.

Evaluating
First, the children should evaluate their own cars using Copymaster 79. Next, as the children were asked to make a moving vehicle, the models should be tested to see whether they actually move. Another way of evaluating the cars is to display them alongside the characters they were designed for and encourage the children to match the cars to their 'owners'. This could even be made into a competition. Failing this, a photograph album of 'Cars of the Stars' could be created using photographs of characters alongside the model cars.

CORREX TOYS

Learning objectives

Designing skills
The children should be given the opportunity to:

- sketch a set of initial ideas
- select and develop one design
- incorporate tabs and slots into their design
- model the design in card or paper
- design and make a set of templates.

Making skills
The children should practise:

- using correx and correx cutters
- using scissors and/or a perforator for scoring
- using a safety ruler and art knife correctly
- joining shapes using tabs and slots
- using resources carefully to minimise waste.

Knowledge and understanding
The children should learn:

- that materials have different properties and differing uses
- how stiff, sheet materials can be made less rigid
- how to adapt correx to make best use of its properties
- how to join materials, such as correx
- that methods of cutting, joining, etc. vary according to the material being used
- to evaluate products made from correx
- to evaluate children's pull-along toys.

Vocabulary: correx, correx cutter, art knife, safety ruler, axle, chassis, spacers, channel, alternate, tabs, slotted, wavy cutter, perforator, straight cutter, template, modelling, modify.

INVESTIGATING TASKS

Materials/equipment needed: Copymasters 80, 81, 82 and 83, correx, kitchen roll, lined paper, wood, pipettes, knitted fabric, card, sandpaper, sanding blocks, a collection of pieces of plastic.

Task 1

Discuss materials in general. Ask the children to imagine they have a piece of an unknown material to describe and test. Brainstorm the possible properties of that material — e.g. heavy, rough, transparent, soft, flexible, cold, shiny, round and record the suggestions in chart form. Then, give each child a piece of correx. Check through the properties listed in the chart and select those that might apply to the correx. Copymaster 81 could be used to reinforce relevant vocabulary and to revise the characteristics of materials.

Task 2

Choose a couple of properties that could be tested, e.g. waterproof qualities, strength and durability. Ask the children to suggest experiments to test these properties. Then carry out some simple experiments such as those outlined below.

● Experiment 1

Using a pipette, drop three drops of water on to a piece of correx and similarly-sized pieces of kitchen roll and lined paper. Compare the differences in puddles made. Use Copymaster 82 to record results.

● Experiment 2

Cut similar lengths of correx, wood and lined paper. (Make sure that the channels on the correx run lengthways along the strip.) Support the lengths on two piles of books, weighted at each end, and test to see how many weights the strips will hold. Repeat the experiment one more time using a strip of correx cut the opposite way — with the channels running across the strip. Use Copymaster 82 to record results.

● Experiment 3

Cut similarly-sized pieces of correx, wool or knitted fabric, thin cardboard and kitchen roll. Pin the pieces securely to a base board using drawing pins or staples. Wrap a strip of sandpaper around a sanding block and rub each piece of fabric. Compare the differences in their appearance after 10 rubs, 50 rubs and 100 rubs. Copymaster 83 can be used to record the results.

Task 3

Make a collection of plastics of different types, thicknesses and colours; objects incorporating some plastic; or different types of pre-school pull-along toys. Using these collections, ask the children to draw each object, state what material it is made of and, if relevant, identify how it is joined together.

Task 4

Copymaster 80 can be used to revise different uses of materials according to their characteristics.

FOCUSED PRACTICAL TASKS

Materials/equipment needed: Copymaster 75, correx (corriflute) scraps, stitch unpickers (correx cutters), metal safety rulers, art knives, guillotine/paper strimmer, glue guns, double-sided tape, sticky pads, cutting mats, stapler, standard punch, dowel, card, MDF wheels, plastic tubing, sandpaper, matchsticks, corrugated card, beads, Blu-tack®/Plasticine.

Introductory tasks

Cutting corex

Demonstrate how correx can be cut with a guillotine or paper trimmer. (Scissors or snips should not be used because they do not make such a neat cut.) If necessary, teach the children how to use the ruler along the end of the trimmer, or how to line up marked correx to ensure a straight, square cut. Then revise how to measure and cut correx using a safety ruler and art knife. Remind the children that they should keep their fingers in the central groove and should always use a self-healing cutting mat or cutting board underneath their work to avoid damaging table tops (Fig. 1). They can then be given a piece of correx and asked to cut a strip. Afterwards, demonstrate how to use a wavy cutter.

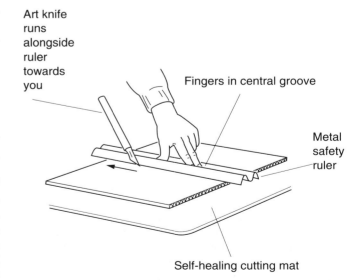

Art knife runs alongside ruler towards you

Fingers in central groove

Metal safety ruler

Self-healing cutting mat

Fig. 1

Next, show the children that a stitch unpicker can be used to slice through the correx channels. Remind them always to place the beaded end inside the channel to avoid damaging the lower layer of plastic (Fig. 2). If the same channel is cut on both sides, the correx will be cut right through and will come apart. This can be useful for cutting a small piece of correx, or if other cutting tools are unavailable. Then ask the children to cut another strip off their piece of correx using this method.

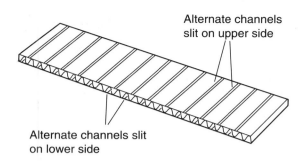

Alternate channels slit on upper side

Alternate channels slit on lower side

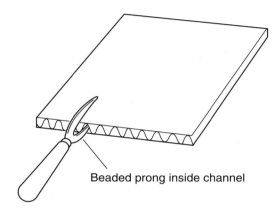

Beaded prong inside channel

Fig. 2

Curving and bending correx
Correx is fairly flexible, but it bends more easily if channelled. Show the children how to cut alternate channels on the same side of a piece of correx. This allows the material to be curved. Using a strip of correx, they should use this technique to bend their correx into a circle (Fig. 3).

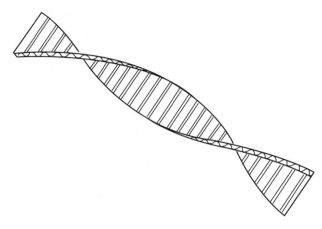

Fig. 4

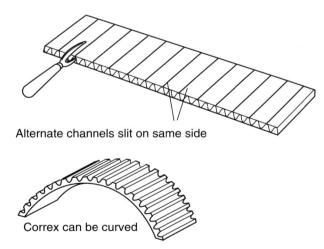

Alternate channels slit on same side

Correx can be curved

Fig. 3

Next, demonstrate how to cut alternate channels on opposite sides of a piece of correx. It is usually easier to cut alternate channels on one side, and then turn over and do the same on the other side. However, it must be stressed that the channels cut on the lower side must be different from the ones cut on the upper side or the whole piece of correx will end up in strips! The correx can then be stretched and twisted into a spiral (Fig. 4). Encourage the children to make their own correx spirals.

Joining and scoring correx
Show the children different ways of joining correx using double-sided tape and sticky pads. Emphasise that PVA glue is not usually suitable for joining plastics. Then demonstrate that correx can be scored with a pair of scissors or a perforator. (The perforator will achieve a more satisfactory mark and allows the correx to bend more easily.) Alternatively, if the correx is slit on one side only, it can be folded to form a right angle. Then squeeze spots of hot glue into the open groove to hold it in place. The join can be neatened with a line of glue along the fold. This method can be used to fix a curve or spiral of correx, as created in the above tasks (Fig. 5). Encourage the children to practise this method using some of their scrap correx. Remind them that it is advisable to roughen smooth surfaces before sticking, as this improves the adhesion.

Demonstrate that two pieces of correx can be joined at an angle by slotting them together. Using a safety ruler and an art knife, measure and cut a slit in the top edge of one piece. This should be the same width as the thickness of the correx, (usually 3-4mm) and reach halfway down the shape. Then cut a similar slit in the lower edge of the other piece and slot the two together. Once they are correctly slotted together, the pieces can be fixed permanently with tape or hot glue (Fig. 6).

Finally, show the children that correx can be punched, stapled and stitched just like thick card.

83

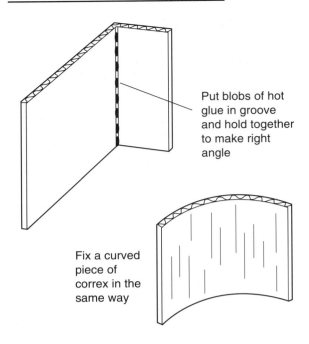

Put blobs of hot glue in groove and hold together to make right angle

Fix a curved piece of correx in the same way

Fig. 5

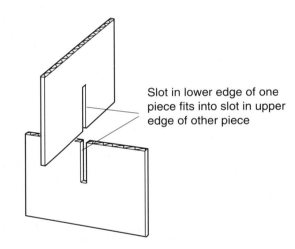

Slot in lower edge of one piece fits into slot in upper edge of other piece

Fig. 6

Independent tasks

In this section, the children will make the correx chassis for a moving vehicle or pull-along toy (Fig. 7). They will each need a rectangle of correx 20cm × 10cm. This can be pre-cut or the children can be asked to do this themselves. However, the channels must run across the width of the rectangle, leaving the ends of the channels visible along the long 20cm sides. Once the correx has

been cut, they can cut four lengths of dowel about 4cm long. (The size of dowel used will depend on the depth of the correx channels, as they need to be the same size.) One end of each dowel piece should be sharpened with a pencil sharpener. This will make it easier to slot the dowel into the correx channels. The pairs of dowel pieces should then be attached to the opposite sides of the chassis to form fixed axles.

Next, the wheels should be attached to the axles. (This is a good opportunity to revise the workings of wheels and axles using Copymaster 75 for support.) Remind the children that when the axles are fixed, as in this case, the wheels must be free to turn. When the axles are loose, however, the wheels must be fixed to the axles so that they turn together. The wheels should be made of thick card, or better still, MDF or plywood. To prevent the wheels from wobbling or rubbing against the chassis, plastic tubing can be cut to form spacers between chassis and wheel. If the wheels do not turn satisfactorily on a smooth surface, they need extra grip. This can be provided by a rubber band (which should be placed around the circumference of the wheel), by sticking a strip of sandpaper to the edge of the wheel, or by gluing pieces of matchstick to the wheel. An alternative would be to glue a strip of corrugated card or correx to the wheel edge, but first the correx must be slit on both sides (as for a spiral) and stretched out, to provide a rough, bumpy surface. To stop the wheels from falling off the axles, beads can be fitted to the ends. Alternatively, blobs of Blu-tack®, Plasticine or hot glue should be used.

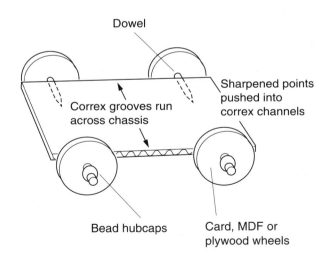

Dowel

Sharpened points pushed into correx channels

Correx grooves run across chassis

Bead hubcaps

Card, MDF or plywood wheels

Fig. 7

84

DESIGN AND MAKE ASSIGNMENT

Aim: To design and make a moving correx toy for a young child.

Materials/equipment needed: a collection of pre-school books, correx in various different colours, dowel, correx cutters, paper trimmer, safety rulers, art knives, snips, chassis (made in Focused practical tasks) glue guns and gluesticks, sticky pads, double-sided tape, thick card/thin paper, scissors, clear tape.

Introduction
Remind the children of the different ways of using correx already discovered. Then discuss the requirements of a toy for toddlers. Have a set of pre-school books available for the children to look at. These may give them ideas for a subject for their design, and also focus their attention on the type and style of pre-school products. Emphasise that their design should be simple, safe and use bold colours. It is possible to select a theme — e.g. animals — on which this work could be based, but it may be easier to ask the group to choose any pre-school or early years' story to link their toy to.

Designing
Remind the children that their design needs to include the 2D chassis made earlier. Ask the children to sketch and colour several of the toy designs. They should then select one design to develop. They will need to redraw their chosen design. Before drawing their final design, they should be encouraged to do some research. If they are following a theme, then a set of topic-related books should be made available. At this stage, stress the need for simplicity in terms of shape and colour of their design. Also, remind them that young children like bold, bright colours, e.g. primary colours. When their drawings are complete, they should be annotated to show how the shapes are to be joined. Tabs will be needed to join pieces together, and particularly to attach the whole shape to the correx chassis.

Encourage the children to model their designs in thick paper or thin card. First, they should draw out all the shapes needed, bearing in mind the slots that may have to be cut, and adding tabs around the sides for gluing.

(If this technique has not been used elsewhere, it should be covered in detail before the designing process begins.) The shapes should then be cut out and attached to the chassis using clear tape. At this point, the card model can be removed and modified. It may be necessary to scrap a card shape and make a new one, and this can be done many times. The children should be encouraged to do this, but should always bear their design in mind rather than change it completely. Any major changes should be noted on the design sheets. Once the child is satisfied with their design, the card pieces should be retained and used as templates.

Making
Using the templates made above, the children should draw out these shapes on the correx. They should be encouraged to use the correx sparingly, avoiding unnecessary wastage. Having already modelled the car body in card, this should be largely avoided anyway. They should then cut out the shapes using safety rulers and art knives, or snips, for those who are less confident. The tabs should be scored and folded, and correx cutters can be used to slit and bend the correx into shape. Hot glue should be used to hold these folds in position. The next stage is to assemble the toy by slotting the pieces of correx together and gluing them in place with hot glue. The whole shape can then be attached to the chassis.

Evaluating
The toys should be tested to see if they do roll along on both smooth and rough floors. They should also be checked for any small parts that may come loose, as this would pose a safety hazard for a small child. Any that pass these two tests could be given a 'kite mark' of approval by the school's authority! (Perhaps it should be mentioned to the children that these toys are not suitable for young children, despite the 'kite mark' approval.) Those toys that pass the tests could then be inspected for general suitability by a local playgroup leader or nursery teacher. Perhaps the school nurse may be able to help out at this stage. Finally, the finished toys should be demonstrated to the rest of the school and displayed with the books that inspired their design.

UNIT 9:
GEARS/PULLEYS

ROUNDABOUTS

Learning objectives

Designing skills
The children should be given the opportunity to:

- investigate things that go round and products that use a pulley
- model mechanisms using construction kits or wood
- draw annotated diagrams, showing materials used
- draw different views of a design
- think about a design brief and devise design criteria
- make a 'shopping list'.

Making skills
The children should practise:

- using a hand drill and drill stand
- measuring and cutting dowel
- planning a sequence of actions, either mentally or on paper.

Knowledge and understanding
The children should learn:

- that a pulley is a wheel with a rope around it
- that a pulley is usually used to lift and lower loads
- that pulleys can be linked together with a belt.

Vocabulary: pulley, belt, follower, driver, axle, load.

INVESTIGATING TASKS

Fig. 1

Materials/equipment needed: two broom handles/ cricket stumps, strong string or rope, model of pulley wheels (see below)/one made from Lego Technic® or BrioMec®, pictures of pulleys and drive belts.

Task 1

Explain that a pulley system is made up of two wheels joined together with a rope or belt. Tie a long piece of string or rope to one of the broom handles. Then wrap the rope around both handles several times, as shown in Fig. 1. Ask two children to hold the broom handles, and to pull away from each other as hard as they can. A third child should try to move the children together by pulling on the free end of the rope. It should be seen that the child pulling the rope can move the other two together fairly easily. This shows the effectiveness of a pulley system. Experimenting with different numbers of turns around the broom handles should show that more turns makes the task easier, but that the child pulling the rope will have to move further.

Task 2

Explain that some machines have pulleys wheels linked together with a belt or chain. This is called the drive belt. Show the children pictures of objects that have pulleys and drive belts. Use a demonstration model, as in Fig. 2, to reinforce this work. Alternatively, make a less permanent model from Lego Technic® or BrioMec®. Identify the drive wheel, follower and belt. Demonstrate that if the drive wheel turns clockwise, the follower also turns clockwise. Afterwards, ask the children to draw or copy a diagram of this movement (Fig. 3).

Task 3

Use the demonstration model again, this time placing the rubber band so that it crosses in the middle. Ask the children to watch the wheels again. They should notice that the follower now turns anti-clockwise. Details of this movement should be added to their original diagram (Fig. 4).

BrioMec® tube or dowel handle slotted into cotton reel

Dowel stuck into holes in base

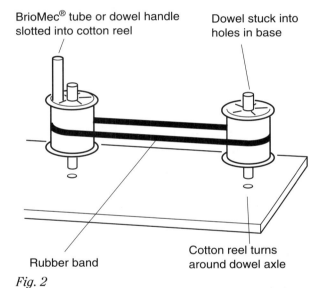

Rubber band

Cotton reel turns around dowel axle

Fig. 2

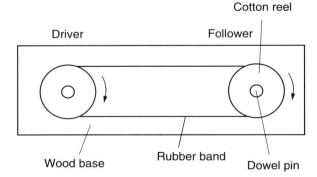

Cotton reel

Driver

Follower

Wood base

Rubber band

Dowel pin

Fig. 3

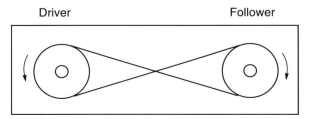

Driver

Follower

Fig. 4

FOCUSED PRACTICAL TASKS

Materials/equipment needed: Copymaster 84, wood scraps, 6mm dowel scraps, cotton reels, rubber bands, junior hacksaws, bench hooks, glue guns, hand drills, beads.

Introductory tasks

Making a pulley system

Provide the children with a piece of scrap wood each. Ask them to mark four dots it. These must be at least 10cm apart. They should then cut four pieces of 6mm dowel (or a similar size that will fit easily through a cotton reel) approximately 6cm long. The next stage is to drill four holes at the four marked points on the wooden base. This is best done in twos, with one child drilling while the other holds the wood firmly. The holes have the same diameter as the dowel so that it fits tightly. The dowel pieces must then be secured in the holes using a spot of glue (Fig. 5).

Once the base is complete, the cotton reels can be placed over the dowel axles. If the cotton reels are in danger of sliding off, beads can be glued on the top of each piece of dowel. The children should then be encouraged to experiment with various ways of linking the reels with rubber bands. They should record their results in diagram form (Fig. 6). Copymaster 84 can be used to record the changes in direction caused by a twisted rubber band.

Answers to Copymaster 84

1. clockwise, 2. clockwise, 3. clockwise, 4. clockwise, 5. anti-clockwise, 6. anti-clockwise, 7. clockwise, 8. clockwise, 9. clockwise, 10. anti-clockwise, 11. anti-clockwise, 12. clockwise, 13. clockwise, 14. clockwise, 15. anti-clockwise

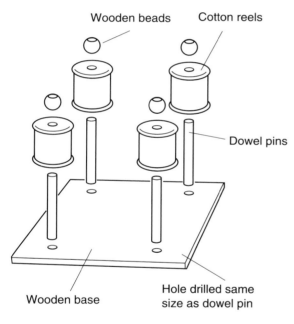

Fig. 5

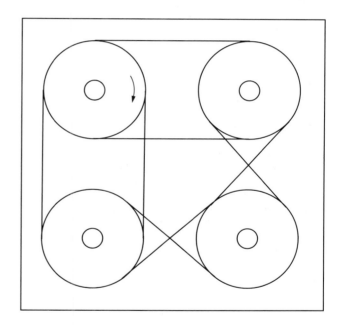

Fig. 6

DESIGN AND MAKE ASSIGNMENT

Aim: To design and make a revolving ride for an 'animal' theme park to be used by play people.

Materials/equipment needed: Copymasters 85 and 86, wood bases approximately 25cm × 8cm, 6mm dowel, cotton reels, correx circles (pre-cut, with a 10cm radius)/paper plates, cardboard inner tubes, card, straws, strong wire/welding rod, wrapping paper, string, PVA glue, glue guns, junior hacksaws, bench hooks, rubber bands, snips, scissors, Connect-O-Mec® tubing, hand drill, drill stand, braid, fringe, beads.

Introduction

Discuss the mechanisms that can be used to make an object revolve, including those covered by the previous tasks. How many different objects can the children think of that revolve? Next, talk about fairgrounds. Ask the class who has been to a fair or theme park recently. Then ask these individuals to describe different rides, including their favourite ones. What is it about these rides that makes them exciting? Afterwards, discuss revolving rides, and explain the design brief. Reuse the model from Investigating tasks (above) to show the children how they could make their ride revolve. Then provide them with a play person to examine. This should be used to make sure that their design is the correct size for its purpose.

Designing

The basic mechanism will be uniform in all designs (Fig 7). It is essential to point out that although the dowel axles are fixed into the base, the cotton reels and anything attached to them must move freely, i.e. nothing must be stuck to the dowel posts.

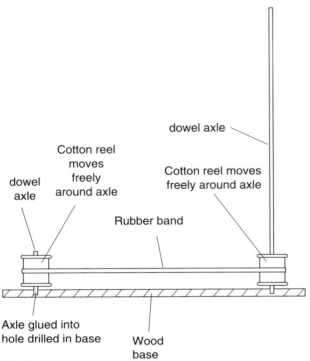

Fig. 7

After having discussed the basic mechanism for the rides, the children should create their designs. (Copymaster 85 provides some useful ideas, although alternatives could be suggested.) Encourage them to go to the library to research and choose an animal theme. They should also consider how their ride will be decorated, e.g. with braid, fringe, sequins and stickers brought from home. Then allow them a few days to

think through their ideas. Next, provide the children with Copymaster 86 and ask them to add the side view of their proposed design to the pre-drawn basic mechanism. They should then label all the materials to be used. Following this, ask the children to write a shopping list. Finally, they should draw a top view of the ride. This will introduce the idea of drawing designs from different angles.

Making

The children should be provided with a wooden base on which two points at least 15cm apart should be marked. Two holes can then be drilled in these places using a hand drill and 6mm drill bit. This is a good opportunity to teach the correct use of the drill and drill stand. Next, ask the children to cut two pieces of dowel to lengths of 6cm and 30cm. These should be stuck into the holes in the base using hot glue. Cotton reels can then be slotted on to the vertical axles and a rubber band placed around them. The next task is to cut a short piece of dowel or Connect-O-Mec® tubing and press this into a groove in the top of one of the cotton reels, to act as a handle. The mechanism should be tested to see if it works. The rubber band may have a tendency to slip off the top or bottom of the cotton reel. If this is the case, a large card wheel with a hole in the centre can be stuck on to the cotton reel, first making sure that the hole is large enough to allow the cotton reel to turn freely around the axle.

From here, the children should be free to follow their own designs, help being given where needed. Encourage them to use the play person when testing their roundabout. This will help them see whether the toy will fit their roundabout and whether the person will stay on or not!

Evaluating

As a class, test each roundabout to see whether the play people will enjoy the ride! Does the roundabout work, and does the toy fit? Is the ride safe for the toy? Encourage the children to discuss each ride, saying whether they would like it, what are its best features, etc. Afterwards, make a class display of the roundabouts and, if possible, invite other classes to view them. They make an excellent display for parents' evening too!

ADVERTISING SIGNS

Learning objectives

Designing skills
The children should be given the opportunity to:

- use their experience of rotary action
- model mechanisms (possibly using a construction kit)
- sketch ideas and select one for development
- consider a design from all angles
- redraw and trace their design several times if necessary
- research lettering styles.

Making skills
The children should practise:

- using a hand drill and drill stand correctly
- measuring and cutting dowel carefully
- cutting and using tabs for sticking
- tracing, copying and using lettering styles, stencils and transfers
- colouring neatly to achieve a good finish
- using a motor in a simple circuit to drive a pulley system
- using the soldering iron, if appropriate.

Knowledge and understanding
The children should learn:

- that pulleys can be used to make things turn
- that similarly-sized pulleys turn at the same speed
- that a large → small pulley system will cause an increase in speed, and the reverse will cause a decrease in speed
- that reversing the polarity of a motor will reverse its direction
- safety rules for using electricity and the dangers of mains electricity.

Vocabulary: pulley, belt, follower, driver, increase, decrease, motor, polarity.

INVESTIGATING TASKS

Materials/equipment needed: Copymaster 87, construction kits incorporating pulley wheels and drive belts (e.g. Lego Technic®) or scraps of wood/wooden bases, pulley wheels, rubber bands, glue guns, dowel, junior hacksaws, bench hooks.

Task 1

The children should construct the following model, either by using a construction kit or materials from the list above (Fig. 1). Ask them to mark a spot on both pulley wheels, and position the wheels so that the spot is at the top, i.e. at 12 o'clock. They should then turn the left-hand pulley wheel — the drive wheel — one revolution and watch the right-hand wheel — the follower (Fig. 2). They should notice that the follower has also completed a full revolution, i.e. they move at the same speed.

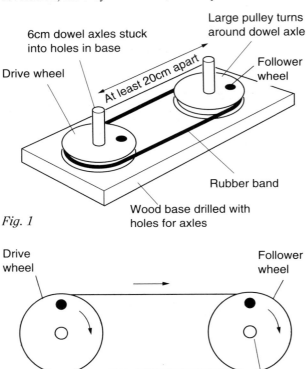

Fig. 1

Fig. 2

Task 2

The children should exchange the two large pulley wheels for two small ones. Then, before repeating the previous experiment, ask them to predict whether the new wheels will move at the same speed as each other or at differing speeds. They should find that they move together (Fig. 3).

Task 3

The follower (right-hand wheel) should be exchanged for a large wheel. Ask the children to turn the left-hand, small, pulley wheel slowly one revolution. They should look to see how far the larger pulley has turned. It should have turned only part of a revolution. Then ask

them to keep turning the small pulley, and to watch the speeds of the two pulleys. They should notice that the small pulley — i.e. the drive wheel — is turning quickly, but the large pulley — the follower — is turning slowly. The speed is being decreased (Fig. 4).

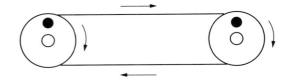

Fig. 3

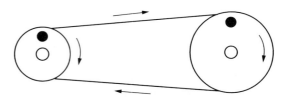

When a small pulley drives a large one, speed decreases.

Fig. 4

Task 4

The children should repeat the previous experiment using the large pulley as the drive wheel. Suggest that they turn the model around, keeping the drive wheel on the left. However, before the experiment takes place, ask them to predict what will happen. They should notice that when turning the large, drive wheel one revolution, the small, follower wheel turns more than one revolution. Ask them to keep turning the wheel, and they should notice that the follower is turning faster than the drive wheel. The speed is being increased (Fig. 5).

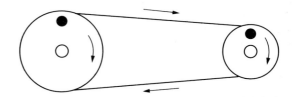

When a large pulley drives a small one, speed increases.

Fig. 5

This activity can be extended by producing a table, as follows, to compare the revolutions, and therefore speeds, of the two wheels.

Number of turns of drive wheel	Number of turns of follower

Task 5

The children should remove the pulleys from their model, and set up a third axle between the other two. The pulleys should be arranged as shown (Fig. 6). If using wooden pulleys, they should be glued together in pairs, with hot glue, while still on the dowel axles. This ensures the correct positioning of the holes, but care must be taken not to get glue on the dowel posts.

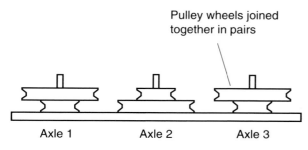

Fig. 6

Ask the children to link the pulleys, as shown in Fig. 7 — i.e. small to large, small to large — using rubber bands. They should then mark a spot on each wheel and position them at 12 o'clock, as before. Next, the drive wheel, on the left, should be turned and the speeds of the pulleys observed carefully. The children should notice that while the wheels on axle 1 move quickly, those on 2 move more slowly and those on axle 3 move the slowest. The movement can be slowed even more by adding more sets of pulleys in the pattern, small to large.

Task 6

The rubber bands should be moved to link the pulleys from large to small. Ask the children to repeat the above experiment, watching the speeds of the pulleys. They should notice that the pulleys on axle 1 move slowly, those on axle 2 move more quickly and those on axle 3 move the quickest. The speed is increased by adding more sets of pulleys in the pattern, large to small (Fig. 8). (Copymaster 87 could be used to reinforce this concept.)

Answers to Copymaster 87

1. B is slower; 2. B is faster; 3. B is same speeed; 4. B is faster; 5. C is slower; 6. C is faster; 7. C is the same speed.

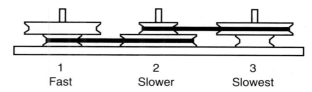

Fig. 7

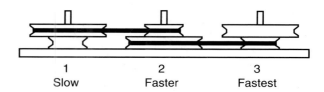

Fig. 8

FOCUSED PRACTICAL TASKS

Materials/equipment needed: 3.2mm dowel, wooden bases, pulley wheels, cotton reels, junior hacksaws, bench hooks, glue guns, rubber bands, motors, motor pulleys, crocodile clip wires, wire cutters/strippers, battery packs, toggle switches.

Introductory tasks

Making a motorised pulley system
Demonstrate how to make this pulley system, then allow the children to make their mechanisms. First, drill two holes in the wooden base. These must be 3.2mm in diameter and at least 10cm apart. Then cut two pieces of dowel, 6cm in length, and glue them into the holes in the base using hot glue. Place a small pulley wheel and a cotton reel on to axle A, and place a large pulley wheel and cotton reel on to axle B. Glue the pulley wheels to the cotton reels with hot glue while still on the axles. This will ensure that the holes are correctly aligned (Fig. 9). Make sure that the glue does not get on to the dowel posts.

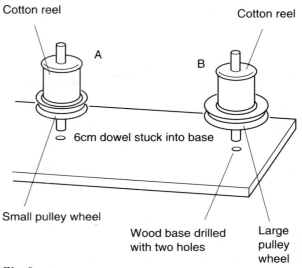

Fig. 9

The next stage is to position a motor, with a motor pulley, on the wooden base. Then attach the motor to a battery, the battery to a switch and the switch to the motor, as shown in Fig. 10. Test the circuit, and ask the children to take note of the speed at which the motor pulley is moving. Then place a rubber band around the motor pulley and first cotton reel at A, and use another one to link the small pulley to the large one at B

(Fig. 11). When the switch is on, the motor should turn the cotton reel, which turns the attached small pulley, which turns the large pulley. The children should notice that the speed is reduced at each stage. Finally, change the connections over on the motor, and ask the children to observe what happens when it is switched on. They should notice that the wheels operate in the opposite direction. This is known as reversing the polarity.

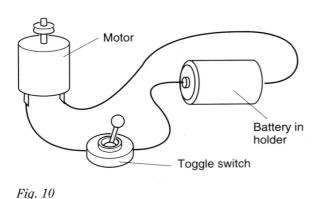

Fig. 10

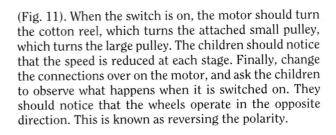

Fig. 11

DESIGN AND MAKE ASSIGNMENT

Aim: To design and make a battery-powered prototype for a revolving shop sign.

Materials/equipment needed: Copymasters 88, 89 and 90, the model made in the Focused practical tasks, correx circles/paper plates, card, poster paints, felt pens, hot glue gun, sticky pads, scissors, a collection of magazine advertisements for well-known products.

Introduction
Show the children the collection of advertisements for well-known products, e.g. Marmite®, Kit-kat®, Dairylea® cheese, Coke®, UHU® etc. Ask them what makes these products recognisable. They should suggest their shape, colour, etc. Then explain the design brief, pointing out that they will be using the motorised pulley system (made in Focused practical tasks) to revolve the sign. Follow this by discussing the types of shop that they might design a sign for, such as a butcher's shop, a bakery, a shoe shop, a post office, a newsagent's, etc. It may be possible to visit the local village or town centre, or at least have some photographs available of them, to inspire the children. They could then design their sign for a specific location rather than generalising. If a local storekeeper can be

invited to visit the school, a more detailed insight can be obtained into the requirements of advertisers. Finally, discuss the characteristics of the signs that the children should take into account, i.e. clear, bold, easily recognisable, simple and colourful.

Designing
Using plain paper the children should be asked to sketch a few ideas for various signs. They should choose a particular shop to advertise and focus on a shape connected with that trade, e.g. a boot for a shoe shop, a bone for a butcher's or a hat for milliner's. Copymasters 88, 89 and 90 may give them some ideas for lettering styles. They should then be encouraged to base their design on this shape.

The sign could be stuck directly on to the turning cotton reel of the motorised mechanism or on to a card or correx circle which is itself attached to the cotton reel. A single design could be placed in the centre of the circle or repeated around the circumference (Fig. 12). If they choose to use a card circle, this will need to be attached to the basic mechanism by tabs (Fig. 13).

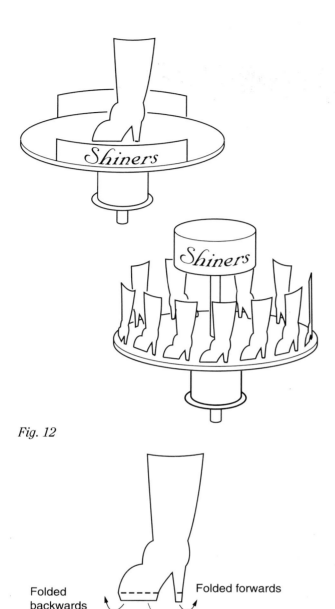

Fig. 12

rubdown transfers are particularly useful, but at this stage transfers should be copied and saved for the final product.

Making

Once designed on paper, the children can begin to transfer their ideas on to card, and then cut them out. If a design is to be repeated, tracings can be used several times. Great care is needed with cutting out the design in order to avoid damaging the tabs. Once cut out, the signs must be carefully lettered and coloured. To make a glossy finish they can be painted with watered-down PVA glue, but this does tend to make some felt pens run. The signs can then be attached to the circle (or other shape) using sticky pads or hot glue. PVA glue is ideal for attaching card circles, but is less reliable when using correx circles. Alternatively, the sign can be made with two separate pieces of card stuck together along the edges, but leaving an unglued channel up the middle which can be slipped over the dowel post (Fig. 14). Finally, the circuit should be connected up, as described in the Focused practical tasks, and the sign should revolve.

Folded backwards

Folded forwards

Tabs added for attaching to base

Fig. 13

Fig. 14

Point out that the signs will be seen from both sides, and so a reverse side will probably be needed, although this does not have to be as detailed as the right side. Also, emphasise that a prospective customer needs to be able to read any writing on the sign as it is revolving.

The children's final design should be drawn to scale on centimetre-squared paper using the cotton reel and squares to achieve an accurate size. It is essential to add the tabs at this point. Also remind the class to add any lettering, and colour it. This would be a good opportunity to revise lettering, including the use of guidelines, centering, shadowing, etc. Stencils or

Evaluating

The design brief specified that the sign should be battery-powered and able to revolve, and so the models should be tested to see whether or not they work. If the children designed their sign for a specific location, the store manager could be invited to view and comment upon the work. Otherwise, the other classes in the school may be invited to see the models on display, preferably in operation. These models are ideal for displaying at school 'team' meetings, assemblies and parents evenings as the initial diagrams, designs, and the models themselves, are all very colourful and appealing.

UNIT 10: CAMS AND CRANKS

MINIBEASTS

Learning objectives

Designing skills
The children should be given the opportunity to:

- sketch several design ideas before selecting one to develop
- draw detailed diagrams to show the making process of a design
- make a 'shopping list' detailing resources needed
- use wheeled toys to aid designing.

Making skills
The children should practise:

- using a hand drill and drill stand
- drilling holes off-centre
- using containers as bases for mechanisms
- bend wire or welding rods
- producing a shopping list with prices.

Knowledge and understanding
The children should learn:

- that simple mechanisms can produce up and down movements and rotational movement
- that a rotational movement can be changed into a reciprocating movement
- to identify a cam and a crank mechanism.

Vocabulary: cam, crank, follower, spindle, rotation, reciprocating.

INVESTIGATING TASKS

Materials/equipment needed: a selection of small, moving toys with simple mechanisms, e.g. pop-up and pull-along toys.

Task 1
Provide each child with a pre-school toy. Ask them to examine the toy to see how it works. They should then draw a diagram of it with annotations that describe how the mechanism works.

Task 2
Ask the children to demonstrate, to the rest of the class, how their toy works.

Task 3
Teach the children how to draw an exploded diagram of their toy, (Fig. 1).

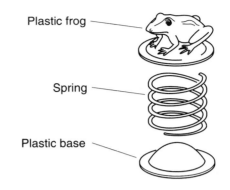

Plastic frog

Spring

Plastic base

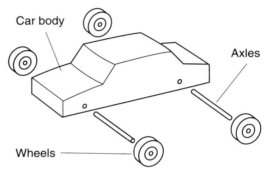

Car body

Axles

Wheels

Fig. 1

FOCUSED PRACTICAL TASKS

Materials/equipment needed: Copymasters 91, 92, 93 and 94; cardboard boxes (at least 10cm square), 50mm and 30mm MDF wheels, 4.5mm dowel, thick wire (e.g. welding rod or florists' wire), 5mm plastic tubing, hacksaws, bench hooks, snips, hand drill and drill stand, paper, drill bits, pliers, thin card, felt pens, beads, revolving punch, PVA glue, scissors.

Independent tasks
These tasks encourage the children to follow a recipe approach to making a pop-up toy. There are two different types of mechanism to be made — the cam and the crank — and so the children should work in pairs, each making a different toy but supporting their partner in the making process.

First, provide the children with Copymasters 91/92 and 93/94 (which should be used as the basis for this activity) and discuss the tasks in detail. They can then begin to make their mechanisms. Allow access to the relevant materials and tools, and give assistance where needed. Particular assistance is likely to be required with the bending of the crank, particularly if using welding rod rather than florists' wire.

DESIGN AND MAKE ASSIGNMENT

Aim: To design and make a minibeast toy that uses a cam or a crank.

Materials/equipment needed: Copymasters 95 and 107, containers (preferably plastic margarine tubs), MDF wheels, dowel, florists' wire/welding rod, thick and thin card, plastic tubing, hacksaws, bench hooks, snips, hand drills, drill stands, paper drills and bits, pliers, felt pens, beads, a revolving punch, PVA glue, scissors, modelling

or emulsion paints/wallpaper paste, newspaper/tissue paper, poster paints, a collection of pre-school toys that use cams or cranks.

Introduction
Show the children the collection of toys and suggest that they examine their mechanisms carefully. Then discuss the design brief and any suggestions that the children might make. They can be directed towards

98

making a minibeast which pulls along on wheels, two of which are cam wheels (Fig. 2); a stationary minibeast with a crank operating a moving head or tail (Fig. 3); or a stationary base with a cam operating a jumping minibeast (Fig. 4).

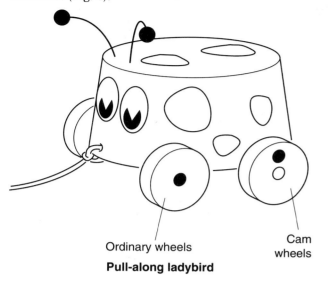

Ordinary wheels   Cam wheels

Pull-along ladybird

Fig. 2

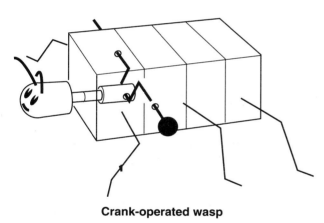

Crank-operated wasp

Fig. 3

Cam-operated jumping spider

Fig. 4

Some children will be proficient enough to combine more than one of these mechanisms or to devise their own version.

Designing

Ask the children to draw a series of sketches showing their initial design ideas. These should be small, but annotated with any thoughts that the children might have. They should then select one of their ideas to develop. Encourage them to choose the one that they will find easiest to make as it will probably be the most successful. They need to redraw this design in more detail, showing all the different working parts. They could draw an exploded diagram. Whatever method of drawing they choose, their diagram should be clearly labelled or a key made to distinguish the components. The children should then make a shopping list detailing all of the materials that they will need. On a separate piece of paper they can list the tools that they will require and write an action plan. Alternatively they could combine these processes to make an instruction leaflet for a minibeast kit (see Copymaster 95).

Making

The first thing that the children need to do is to collect their materials. Initially, they should be allowed to have only those listed on their shopping lists. Anything that they need later can be added to the list, but they should be encouraged to plan ahead and to reduce the amount of resources used. The children should then begin making the mechanism for their models, following a similar method to that used to make the 'cam clown' and 'crank creature'. When this is complete, the children can consider the decoration of their model. There are two obvious ways to decorate the base of the model. The first is to cover the base with a papier-maché style mix of wallpaper paste and tissue paper or newspaper. This will harden and be kept in place by the axle and/or crank. The alternative is to paint the base first with a layer of white emulsion paint and then modelling paint/poster paints, permanent marker pens, sticky labels, sequins, etc. However, if the container is very flexible, the paint may tend to crack in time.

Evaluating

The children should be asked to evaluate their own projects by highlighting the areas which went well and those that went badly. They should then be asked to list any differences between the original design idea and the finished product. They should also list any additional resources that they used. Copymaster 107 can be used to support this work. The children could be encouraged to evaluate each other's projects by working in pairs and writing a critical evaluation of their partner's model. This should include descriptions of how the model works, whether it works well, the quality of finish and visual appeal.

TECHNIQUES, TOOLS AND STORAGE

This section is designed to serve as a source of reference for the rest of the book. It contains guidance on the use of tools and descriptions of various techniques used in the designing and making processes.

Many of the tasks in Design and Technology require the use of potentially hazardous tools, and so this section also serves to reinforce aspects of health and safety.

This section contains information on the following:
- Design techniques
- Making techniques
- Tools
- Storage ideas

DESIGN TECHNIQUES

Investigate existing products to collect ideas

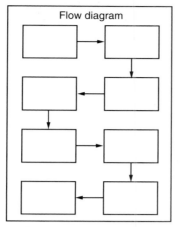

Draw a flow diagram for sequencing actions

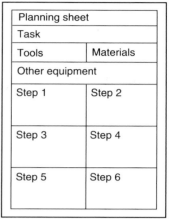

Devise a step-by-step plan

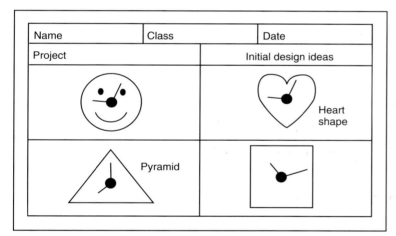

Produce quick, initial sketches

Use isometric paper for 3D diagrams

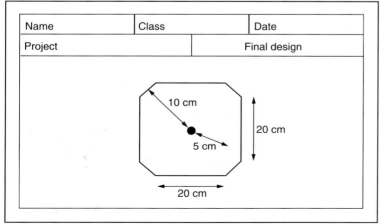

Draw detailed scale diagrams of final idea

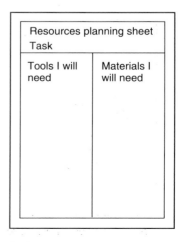

101

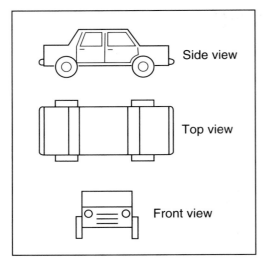

Side view

Top view

Front view

Draw different views of object

Survey		
1	✓✓	
2		
3	✓✓✓	
4	✓✓	
5	✓✓	
6	✓✓✓✓	
7	✓	
8	✓	

Survey preferences

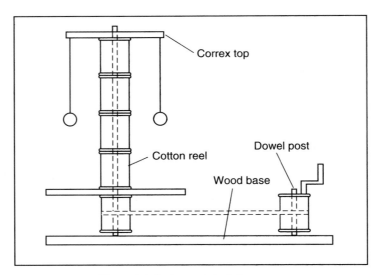

Correx top

Cotton reel

Dowel post

Wood base

Draw detailed annotated diagrams

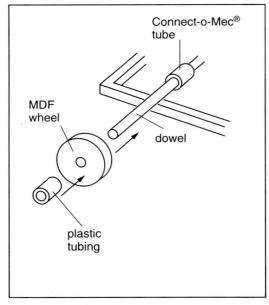

Connect-o-Mec® tube

MDF wheel

dowel

plastic tubing

Draw exploded diagrams to show how things fit together

Model designs using card, paper, mouldable materials or construction kits

102

MAKING TECHNIQUES

Frameworks

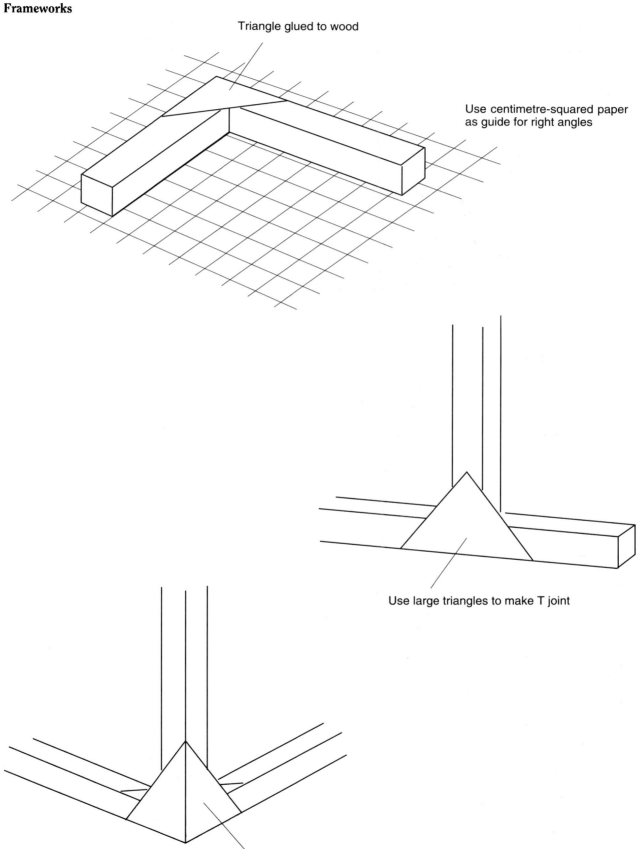

Triangle glued to wood

Use centimetre-squared paper as guide for right angles

Use large triangles to make T joint

Large triangle stuck to support upright

103

Joints

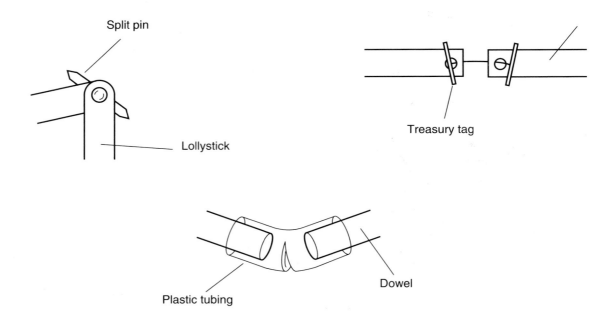

Split pin

Lollystick

Treasury tag

Plastic tubing

Dowel

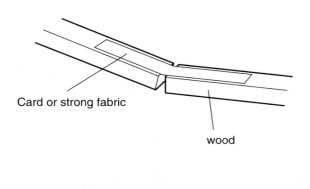

Card or strong fabric

wood

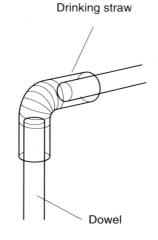

Drinking straw

Dowel

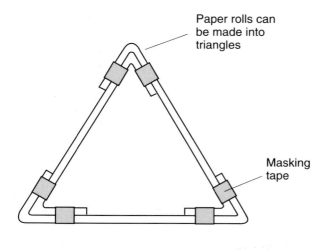

Paper rolls can
be made into
triangles

Masking
tape

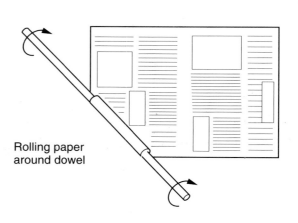

Rolling paper
around dowel

Wheels, axles and hubcaps

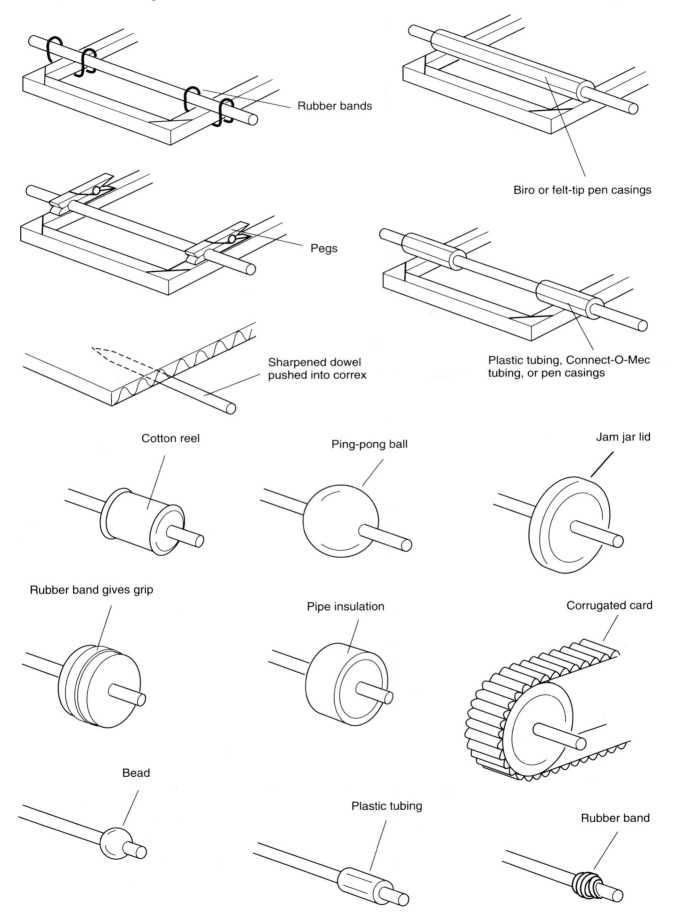

Rubber bands

Biro or felt-tip pen casings

Pegs

Plastic tubing, Connect-O-Mec tubing, or pen casings

Sharpened dowel pushed into correx

Cotton reel

Ping-pong ball

Jam jar lid

Rubber band gives grip

Pipe insulation

Corrugated card

Bead

Plastic tubing

Rubber band

Electricity

Battery holder

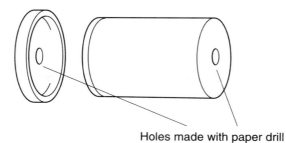

Holes made with paper drill

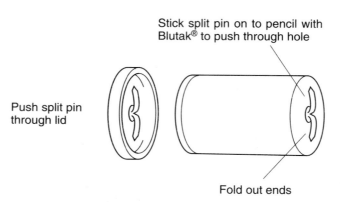

Push split pin
through lid

Stick split pin on to pencil with
Blutak® to push through hole

Fold out ends

Wrap wire around
split pin on lid
Put battery inside
and push on lid

Wrap wire around
split pin and fold long
ends under to make it
neater

106

Switches

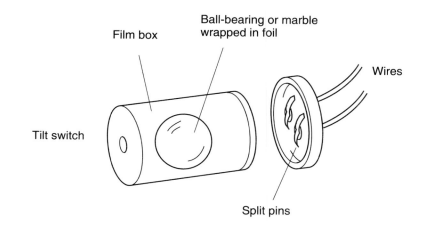

Film box

Ball-bearing or marble wrapped in foil

Wires

Tilt switch

Split pins

Simple switches

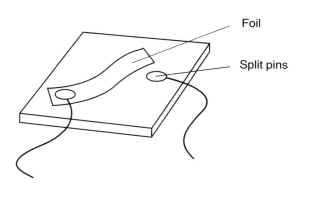

Foil

Split pins

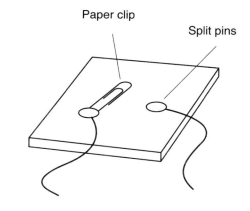

Paper clip

Split pins

Pressure switch

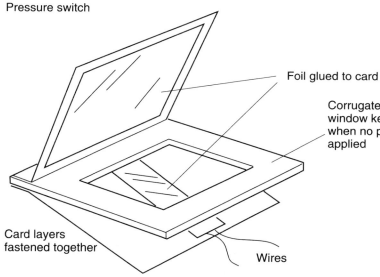

Foil glued to card

Corrugated card window keeps foil apart when no pressure is applied

Card layers fastened together

Wires

Press switch

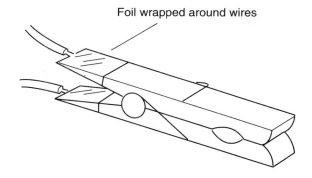

Foil wrapped around wires

Motor clips

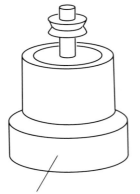

Plastic pipe or cut-down syringe
casing holds motor upright

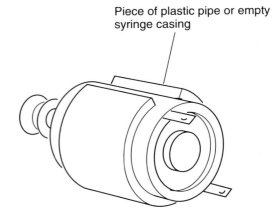

Piece of plastic pipe or empty
syringe casing

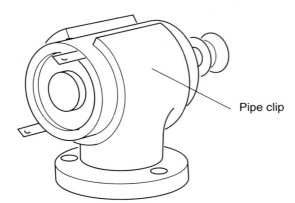

Pipe clip

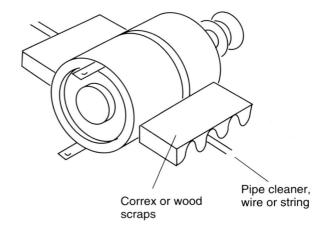

Correx or wood
scraps

Pipe cleaner,
wire or string

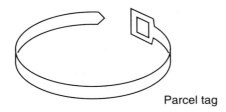

Parcel tag

Cutting tools

Fingers in
central groove

Self-healing
mat

Correx cutter

Safety ruler

Run correx cutter
along groove

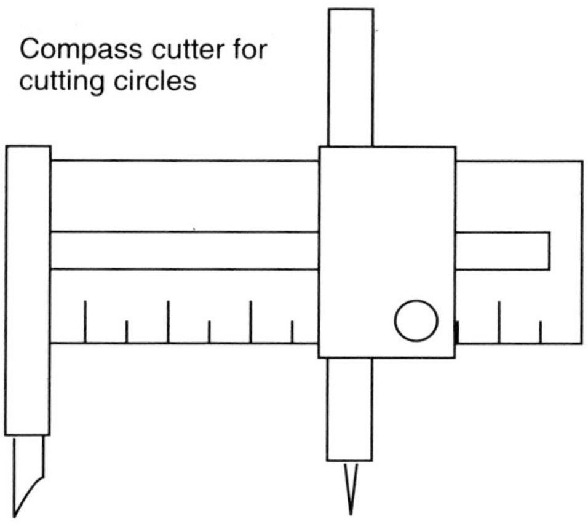

Compass cutter for
cutting circles

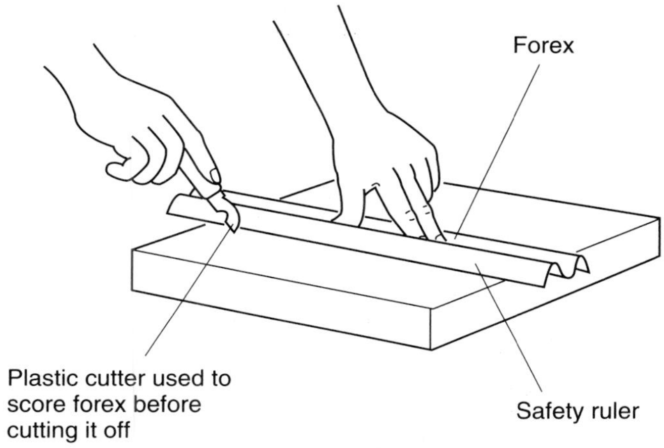

Forex

Plastic cutter used to
score forex before
cutting it off

Safety ruler

paper drill

Unscrew to
change drill bit

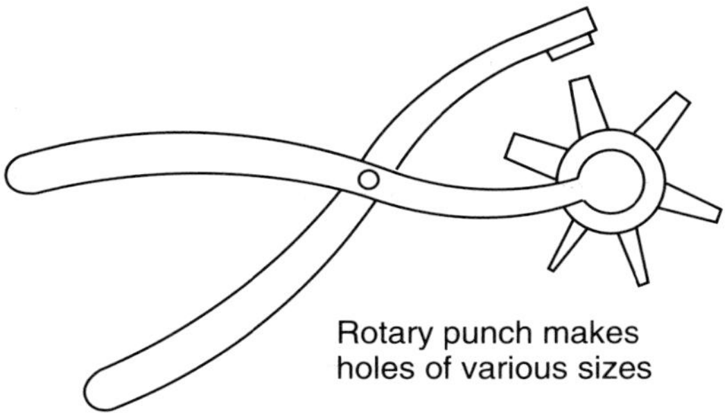

Perforator   Wavy cutter   Rotary cutter

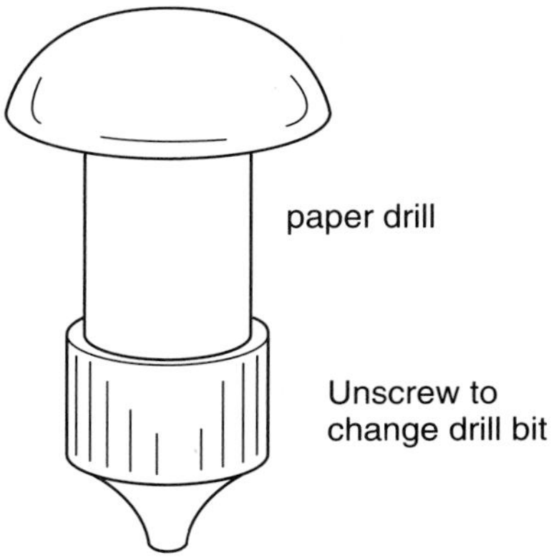

Rotary punch makes
holes of various sizes

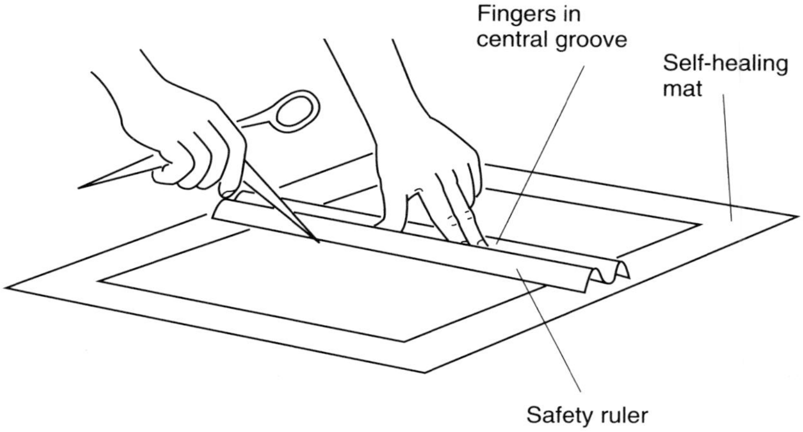

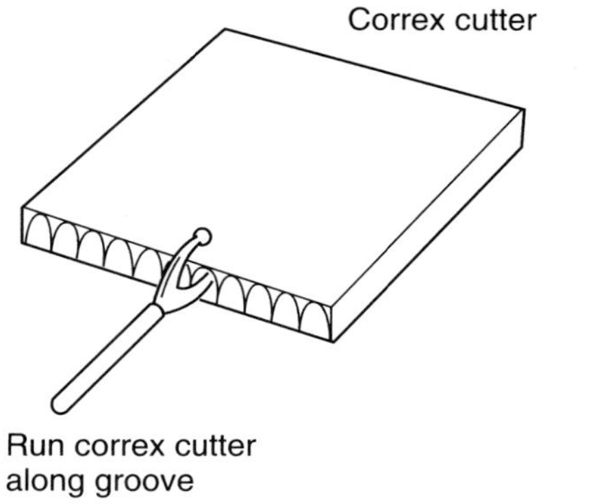

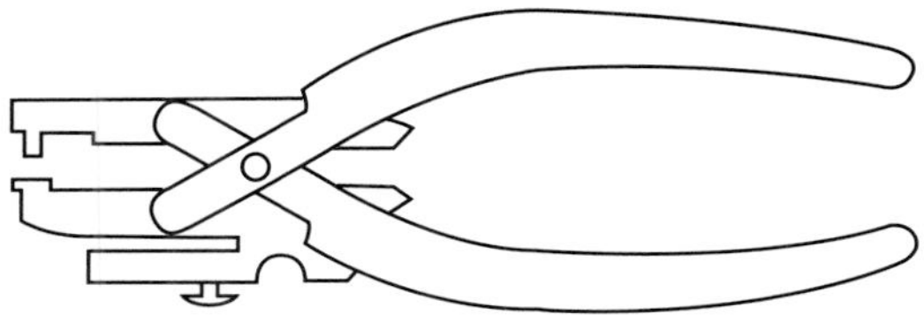

Eyelet-pliers punch

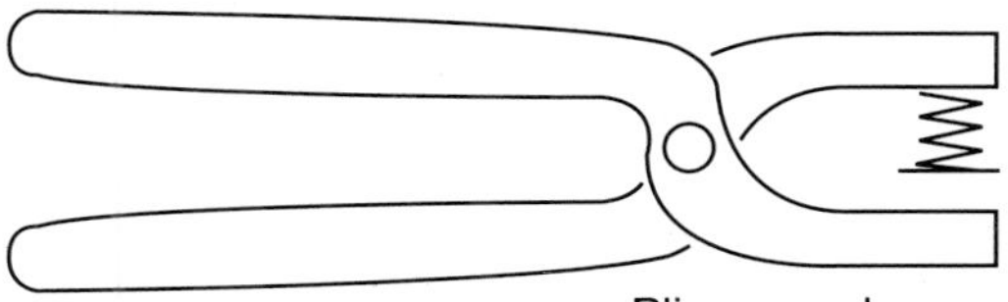

Pliers punch

Use of wire strippers

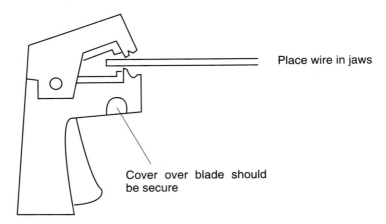

Place wire in jaws

Cover over blade should be secure

Squeeze handles without pulling to strip away plastic insulation

Use of bench hook, hacksaw and solo clamp

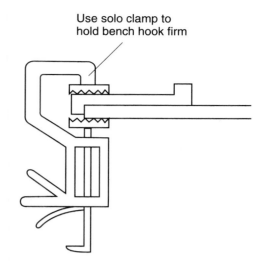

Use solo clamp to
hold bench hook firm

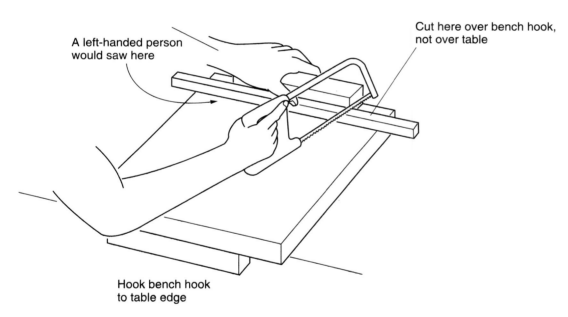

A left-handed person
would saw here

Cut here over bench hook,
not over table

Hook bench hook
to table edge

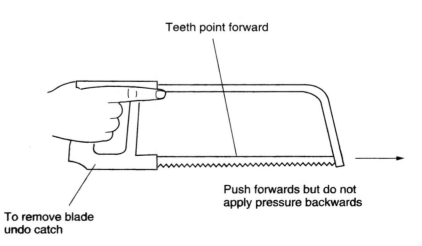

Teeth point forward

To remove blade
undo catch

Push forwards but do not
apply pressure backwards

Use of hand drill

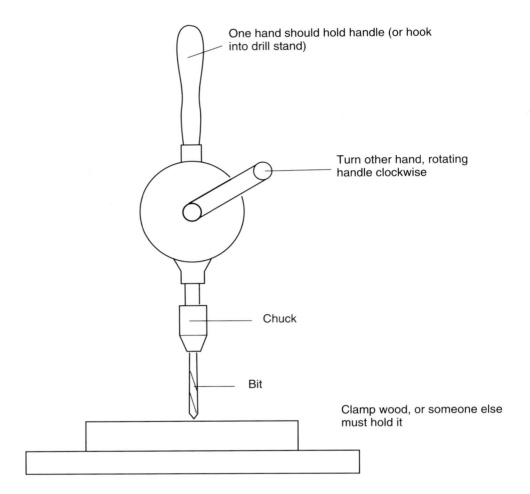

One hand should hold handle (or hook into drill stand)

Turn other hand, rotating handle clockwise

Chuck

Bit

Clamp wood, or someone else must hold it

Put scrap wood under to protect table, or put a cork on drill bit to act as a stop

End view

After hole is drilled, keep turning clockwise to withdraw drill bit

To change drill bit, hold drill steady and grasp chuck tightly
Turn rotating handle firmly anti-clockwise to loosen jaws
Replace drill bit and turn chuck to close jaws

Fasten by holding chuck and turning rotating handle sharply clockwise again

Use of shaper saw

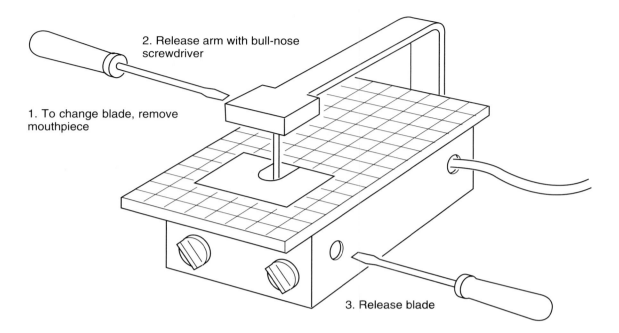

2. Release arm with bull-nose screwdriver

1. To change blade, remove mouthpiece

3. Release blade

4. Replace blade by inserting into lower clamp first and tighten screw
5. Lower arm on to top end of blade, insert blade into clamp and tighten

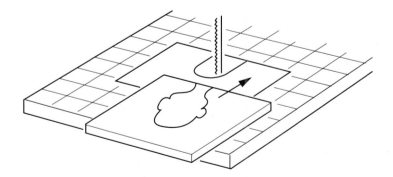

Guide forex gently forwards
Do not push against blade or pull forex back

Use of the soldering iron

Solder

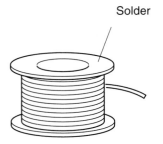

Beware, tip stays hot for several minutes after the iron is switched off

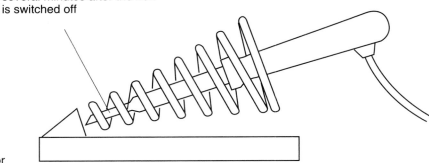

Damp sponge for cleaning soldering iron

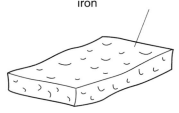

Motor

1. Clean iron when hot
2. Clamp wire still and heat wire with tip of iron. Hold solder to wire and allow it to melt. This is called 'tinning the wire'
3. Position wire so that it touches the electrical connection and clamp
4. Hold wire on to connection with tip of soldering iron. Allow solder to flow onto connection, holding wire in place
5. Remove iron and allow to cool

Wire

Solder

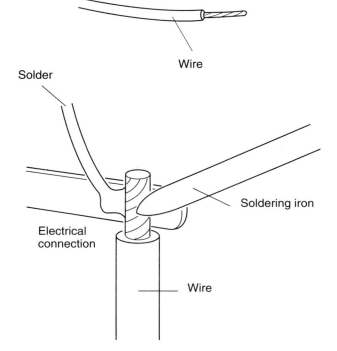

Electrical connection

Soldering iron

Wire

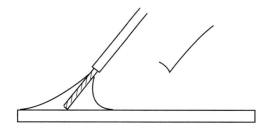

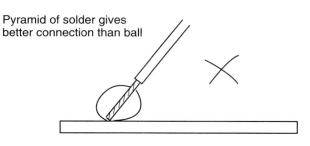

Pyramid of solder gives better connection than ball

STORAGE IDEAS

Store glue in chocolate sauce pots

The pin in the lid prevents the glue drying up

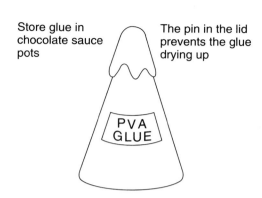

PVA GLUE

Drainpipe lengths are ideal for storing wood. Lengths longer than 1m should be stored flat to prevent warping

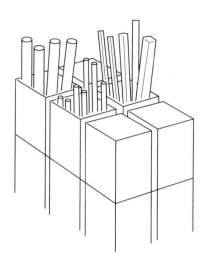

ELECTRICITY KIT 3

Old fruit and vegetable baskets are often available from green grocers and supermarkets

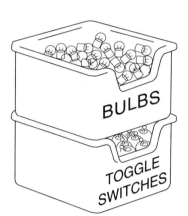

BULBS

TOGGLE SWITCHES

Small stacking boxes are ideal for storing small components

FABRIC PIECES

PVC TUBING

Store large materials in plastic bins

Make a labelled tool board for groups of tools.

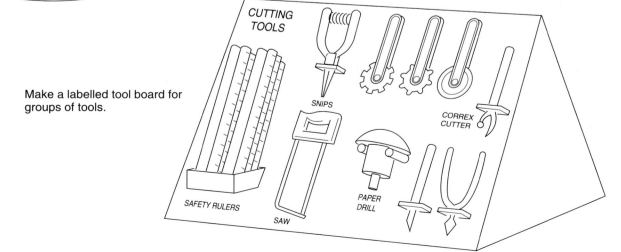

CUTTING TOOLS

SNIPS

CORREX CUTTER

SAFETY RULERS

SAW

PAPER DRILL

115

RESOURCES CHECKLIST

Tools
Scissors
Hole punch
Stapler
Junior hacksaws and blades
Hammers
Hand drill and bits
Drill stand
Bench hooks
Screwdriver
Correx cutters
Plastic cutter
Wire strippers
Terminal screwdriver
Shaper saw and blades
Snips
Solo clamps
Glue guns (low temperature)
Dust masks and goggles
Side cutter
Soldering iron
Compass, rotary, perforation, wavy and circle cutters
Art knives
Safety rulers
Paper drill
Eyelet pliers, pliers and revolving punches
Self-healing mat

Electrical equipment
1.5V bulbs
Clip bulb holders
Batten bulb holders
Battery holders
Film cases
Buzzers
Motors (1.5V)
Motor pulleys
Bell-push switches
Toggle switches
Reed switches
Crocodile clip wires
Multi-strand wire

Terminal block/circuit connectors
Clock mechanisms

Materials
Wood e.g. Jelutong (10mm and 6mm)
Dowel (various diameters)
Correx
Forex
Fabric pieces
Braid
Foil
Pipe lagging
Reclaimed materials e.g. boxes, bottles
Clay

Other resources
Lollysticks
Clothes pegs
Photocopied card triangles
MDF wheels (various sizes)
Pulley wheels (various sizes)
Card wheels (various sizes)
Cotton reels
Wooden beads
Flexible PVC tubing
Gluesticks
Masking tape
Double-sided sticky pads
Sandpaper
Paper clips
Split pins
Pipe cleaners
Modelling wire
Connect-O-Mec® tubing
String
Clear tape
PVA glue
Felt pens
Drinking straws
Treasury tags
Rubber bands
Laminated centimetre-squared paper
Construction kits